Time

Time

Selected Lectures on Time and Relativity, the Arrow
of Time and the Relation of Geological and Biological
Time and on Men of Science

Edited by

S. T. BUTLER, M.SC., PH.D., D.SC.
Professor of Theoretical Physics, University of Sydney

and

H. MESSEL, B.A., B.SC., PH.D.
*Professor of Physics and Head of the
School of Physics, University of Sydney*

PERGAMON PRESS

OXFORD · LONDON · EDINBURGH · NEW YORK
PARIS · FRANKFURT

Pergamon Press Ltd., Headington Hill Hall, Oxford
4 & 5 Fitzroy Square, London W.1

Pergamon Press (Scotland) Ltd., 2 & 3 Teviot Place, Edinburgh 1

Pergamon Press Inc., 44-01 21st Street, Long Island City, New York 11101

Pergamon of Canada Ltd., 6 Adelaide Street East, Toronto, Ontario

Pergamon Press S.A.R.L., 24 rue des Ecoles, Paris 5e

Pergamon Press GmbH, Kaiserstrasse 75, Frankfurt-am-Main

Printed in Great Britain by the Ipswich Litho Press Ltd.

INTRODUCTION

We have chosen Time as the main theme for the 1965 Nuclear Research Foundation Summer Science School for high-school students as we know that students and even more people generally have an increased desire for knowledge in this fascinating topic.

The lecture material of our 1965 Summer Science School contained in the chapters of this book is therefore concerned primarily with the concept of time on earth and in the universe generally.

The main theme of time is expounded by two of the world's leading cosmologists, Professor Hermann Bondi, of London University, and Professor Thomas Gold, of Cornell University, U.S.A. Their lectures are built on the foundations laid by earlier lectures by ourselves.

Our lectures develop the relation of geological and biological time and also give an introduction to Einstein's theory of relativity, which forms the basis for the concept of time in the universe.

Upon these foundations Professor Bondi builds four lectures on time and relativity, including an introduction to his famous k calculus.

The final four lectures on this theme are by Professor Gold who expounds the concept of the fourth dimension, the Arrow of Time and its theoretical reversibility.

Because all these lectures have been specifically prepared, written and edited for fourth-year high-school students, we feel that they will be of interest not only to them but to the widest sections of the public. We feel that the material as presented will be appreciated not only by the increasingly more science-conscious layman in this scientific age but also, in fields other than his own, by the specialised scientist.

Finally the book also contains a section written by the well-known Professor Julius Miller, who through his ingenious demonstrations of physical phenomena has done so much to enthuse young and old the world over in the cause of science.

His section tells of Great Men of Science who have been commemorated on international postage stamps, and in an appendix Professor Miller does what he likes best — he asks scores of questions to fire the mind about the wonders of nature.

The 1965 Nuclear Research Foundation Summer Science School and, indeed, this book are intended to stimulate and develop science consciousness in Australia generally and particularly in the 150 outstanding fourth-year high-school students of 1964 who have won scholarships to attend the Summer School. The Foundation wishes to applaud and reward their ability and diligence.

Lastly, we accept complete responsibility for the contents of this book and apologise for any errors which may have crept into the texts.

S. T. BUTLER and H. MESSEL

Sydney, January, 1965.

CONTRIBUTORS OF LECTURES

H. BONDI

Professor of Applied Mathematics,
King's College, University of London

S. T. BUTLER

Professor of Theoretical Physics,
University of Sydney

T. GOLD

Professor of Astronomy,
Cornell University, Ithaca, N.Y., and
Director of the Cornell University Center for
Radiophysics and Space Research

H. MESSEL

Professor of Physics and Head of the School
of Physics, University of Sydney

J. S. MILLER

Professor of Physics,
El Camino College, University of California

CONTENTS

THE SPONSORS

The Nuclear Research Foundation within the University of Sydney gratefully acknowledges the generous financial assistance given by the following group of individual philanthropists and companies, without whose help the 1965 Summer Science School for fourth-year High School students and the production of this book would not have been possible.

Ampol Petroleum Limited

H. G. Palmer, Esq.

Plessey Pacific Pty. Limited

W. D. & H. O. Wills (Aust.) Limited

Dr. S. Goldberg,

      and

Philips Electrical Industries Pty. Limited

Time and the Universe

(Six Chapters)

S. T. BUTLER and H. MESSEL

(Right)

S. T. BUTLER
*Professor of Physics
(Theoretical),
University of Sydney.*

(Left)

H. MESSEL
*Professor of Physics,
Head of the
School of Physics,
University of Sydney.*

CHAPTER 1

Time on Earth

A Timeless World

The passage of time is something familiar to all of us. The days come and go, and with each passing day we grow older. In this highly mechanised world of today innumerable clocks and watches ceaselessly tick away time and determine the schedules by which hundreds of millions of people live.

The passage of time is thus a concept which is second nature to us, and which all of us understand thoroughly. Or do we? Before reaching out into the universe and considering what time means in the universe in general, let us take stock a little and make sure that we appreciate fully the concept of time on earth— this concept that appears to us so natural and which, we believe, would also have appeared natural to earliest man. To do this, we shall consider a story which will help to highlight some of the points we wish to make.

Have you ever wondered what life on earth would be like if our planet were not spinning rather rapidly on its axis but always presented the same face to the sun? It can be very amusing and instructive if you think about this a little. Let us use a few facts which you probably already know.

In this situation the earth could be said to possess captured rotation. Captured rotation is not unusual in the solar system; the planet Mercury always presents the same face to the sun, and there is even a possibility that Venus does the same. Recent observations of Venus have indicated that this planet either has captured rotation or is spinning very slowly. Then again the moon in its orbit around the earth always presents the same face to us.

It is known that the spinning of the earth is very gradually slowing down. This is due to the gravitational influence of both the sun and the moon producing tides in the earth's oceans and atmosphere, and the energy which goes into these tides is gradually being taken from the energy of rotation of the earth's spin. The rate of slowing down of the earth's spin is, however, so slow that the length of one of our days is increasing by only a few thousandths of a second each year. In a few thousand million years' time however, provided the solar system still remains in existence, the earth also may always present the same face to the sun.

Obviously, this is so far away that it need cause us little concern. Suppose, however, that the earth's rotation had stopped a few million years ago and that life on earth had evolved under these conditions. We would have the earth with the same half always turned towards the sun; the opposite half would always look out on the darkness of space. On the side facing the sun there would be eternal day, and on the opposite side, eternal night. At any one place on the earth conditions would always be the same; there would be no alternating day and night and there would be no seasons to break the monotony.

On the sunlit side the scorching rays from the sun would long since have evaporated any sea water and turned the ocean beds into vast deserts of salt. The evaporated water would also long since have been carried by winds to the dark side, condensed into clouds and deposited as snow, and the dark side would be permanently covered with a layer of ice several thousand feet thick.

Thus the earth would simply have a day side with interminable desert beneath a motionless scorching sun, and a night side with its perpetual coating of ice, and temperature far below anything that occurs on earth today even at the South Pole.

At any point on the lighted side, the sun would appear to be completely motionless. On the border between the dark and lighted side the sun would appear just on the horizon but always in the same spot. Here the temperature would be about the same as at our North or South Pole. If someone set out from this region into the day side he would first cross a temperate zone about 1,500 miles in breadth. In this zone there would be rivers formed by melting ice from the dark side and flowing towards the vast salt desert; here they would evaporate and form clouds and make their way back to the frozen side. If our traveller continued further into the day side the country would get drier and hotter and the sun grow fiercer all the time so that before long it would be impossible for him to continue. The temperature would soon become so high that our own Sahara Desert would seem cool by comparison.

Conditions would be just as trying for someone attempting to force an entry to the frozen side of the globe. Everything would be covered with thick ice, icy winds would be blowing and thermometers would freeze.

The only possible inhabitable area on the earth would be a band perhaps a little over 2,000 miles in breadth running right round the earth in the region separating the day side from the night side. Here there would be soil and water and it would be possible for life to evolve and to thrive, and possibly for rational beings—but probably not humans as we know them—to exist. Close to the ice it would be as cold, for example, as Northern Norway and on the other edge of this inhabitable strip it would be like the hot, dry regions of North Africa. There would be a rapid increase in temperature from the cold side of this area to the hot side—a temperature rising from about freezing to perhaps 100 degrees Fahrenheit across the mere 2,000 mile width.

You may be surprised though that this area, which would be available to living creatures, would be almost exactly the same as the total land area on earth today, so that abundant life could exist. The main difference would be the absence of marine life, although there would be some fresh water fish in the rivers. Under such conditions the living population of the earth would not be grouped together on a number of separate continents; instead the land would simply be the continuous strip right around the earth through which rivers would run from the cold towards the hot side.

You can, no doubt, imagine many differences between what life would be like on the earth under these conditions and what it actually is like. If you think for a moment, you will realise that perhaps the most important difference would be the apparent lack of any passage of time. Apart from the movement of living things, everything in this world would appear completely stationary—the sun would appear to be stationary and the earth would appear to be stationary. With the dark side being inaccessible to living things they would not be able to see any stars, and they would have no idea whatsoever of the vast expanse of outer space. To these inhabitants the entire universe would simply appear to be the earth and the stationary sun.

All this would be true apart from one minor exception. At intervals, a pale sickle-shaped moon would show up on the horizon of the day sky, travel towards the sun growing thinner and thinner, then waxing again and disappearing on the other side. You can imagine what myths there might be about this phenomenon—perhaps similar to the early myths which arose here on earth about the sun, the moon and the stars.

Life under these conditions would be very different from that to which we are accustomed. We know that the sun rises each morning and that we perhaps have to catch a bus or a train at a certain time in order to arrive at school or at work on time. A large percentage of the world's inhabitants still regulate their lives about the rising and the setting of the sun. In our story, however, everything is always the same, and there would be no natural time periods occurring. The inhabitants would have to regulate their lives by methods of their own for sleeping and resting and another time for working. Until the advent of artificial devices—clocks—life would be very haphazard indeed; the only indication of the passage of time would be a biological one, indicated by the fact that individuals would gradually be growing older and older and eventually die.

As the living beings in our story became more and more advanced, they might realise the great convenience in aiding them to regulate their lives if they could devise means of measuring the regular passage of time. They could, for example, devise a gadget such as an hour-glass and set up as their unit of time the time taken for a given quantity of fine sand to run from one container down into another. Later they might notice that a pendulum swings at a steady rate and they might invent clocks which would tick away at a regular rate.

The purpose of such clocks would be to enable the inhabitants to regulate their lives. There is no way of judging what their unit of time would be, except that it would almost certainly have nothing to do with our hours, days or years. There would be no natural phenomena that they knew about, to guide them at all. Eventually they might perfect a system of time tables which could be published and on which the civilization could operate.

In due time, of course, we might imagine our rational beings becoming so advanced as to have factories, methods of travel and eventually even aircraft. When this happened it would be within their power to make a great scientific discovery. An exploring 'plane might first take a trip across the day side flying sufficiently high for the temperature to remain cool. The crew of this exploring 'plane would then simply see the vast deserts and salt areas beneath them. Later on, however, a 'plane with full temperature control could fly into the dark side and the amazed crew could see the multitude of stars. If our beings had by this time acquired the full curiosity and spirit of inquiry of a scientifically-minded race, it would not be long before they embarked on the enormous task of setting up manned outposts—observing stations somewhere on the great ice pack of the dark side. Conditions there would be so difficult that this would be for them a venture almost as great as it is for us to set up a manned outpost on the moon. All travel to the outpost would have to be undertaken in enclosed temperature-controlled containers, and the observing station itself would have to be an enclosed unit with its own temperature control and with food transported from the inhabited strip.

At this point the field of astronomy would be born, and probably after generations of observations, the scientists and mathematicians would finally unravel the picture of the universe as we have it today. They would realise for the first time that the earth is simply one planet in orbit around the sun; they would realise that gravitational fields must exist; they would realise that even the sun is but one of a hundred thousand million suns in our galaxy—and that the universe consisted of innumerable galaxies extending as far as can be seen.

In doing this, of course, they would realise that their planet revolved in an orbit around the sun and, for the first time in their history, they would have a natural unit of time—the year.

The Actual World

Such problems as we have discussed have never arisen for man on earth, since the earth is not only spinning but is doing so on an inclined axis. Throughout all our history man has had two obvious

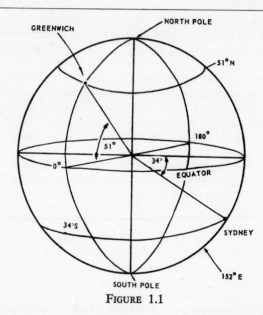

GREENWICH

NORTH POLE

51°N

180°

51°

0°

34°

EQUATOR

34°S

SYDNEY

152°E

SOUTH POLE

FIGURE 1.1

and natural units of time, the day and the year. The day is an easy period of time to recognise because we experience daylight and darkness as a result of the spin of the earth on its axis. The year also has always been a relatively easy period of time to recognise because of the seasons—caused by the tilting of the earth's axis. Speaking in a general way, we say a day is the period of time for one complete revolution of spin of the earth, and the year is the time taken for the earth to make one complete revolution around the sun. It does this in just under 365¼ days. We shall sharpen up these definitions of time later in this chapter.

It is completely natural, therefore, that firstly the day and secondly the year should be used by man to measure the passage of time. For accurate time measurements during a day, the duration of each day has been divided by 24 to give us hours and these in turn are divided by 60 to give us minutes and these again by 60 to give seconds.

At any one spot on the earth's surface we call the time 12 o'clock or 12 noon when the sun is most nearly overhead. It is clear therefore, that the actual time as shown by clocks will be different at different points on the earth's surface. If it is 12 o'clock or noon at one place it will be midnight at the place on the opposite side of the earth.

In order to see how times vary, it is convenient to draw circles around the earth passing through the Poles, as indicated in *Figure 1.1*. Each circle is called a meridian. Let us compare two meridians such as, for example, the one passing through Greenwich, the observatory near London in England, and the one passing through Sydney—as shown in *Figure 1.1*. If one swung the meridian through Greenwich around to Sydney we would be moving it eastward through 152°. This is described by the term *longitude* and Sydney is said to have a longitude of 152° east of Greenwich. It is clear that, with the earth rotating so that Sydney is moving eastward towards the right hand side of *Figure 1.1,* Sydney will see the sun at an earlier time than Greenwich by an amount depending on the 152° of longitude. In fact we can easily work out that one complete revolution of 360° corresponds to one day which is 24 hours. Thus every degree of revolution of the earth corresponds to $\dfrac{24 \times 60}{360} = 4$ minutes of time.

Thus, Sydney must be $152 \times 4 = 608$ minutes ahead of Greenwich in time. By tradition Greenwich has been taken to have zero degrees longitude and the longitude of all other places on the earth is given as so many degrees east or west of Greenwich. It was F. G. W. Struve (1793-1864), the Director of the famous Pulkovo observatory near Leningrad, who took the decisive step towards the international recognition of Greenwich as the prime meridian. Places are said to be east of Greenwich if they have a longitude less than 180° east of Greenwich and the times of these places are ahead of that at Greenwich. In this way one-half of the earth's surface has longitude east of Greenwich. The other half of the earth's surface has longitude of anything up to 180° west of Greenwich, and the times of all these places lag behind that of Greenwich.

If you start from the longitude at Greenwich therefore and work eastward you can readily work out how far ahead of Greenwich any place is in time. A place which has a longitude of 45° east is

3 hours ahead of Greenwich; a place which is 90° east has time 6 hours ahead of Greenwich; and finally a place which is almost 180° east is 12 hours ahead of Greenwich in time.

Similarly, if we work back the other way, 45° west of Greenwich means 3 hours behind Greenwich time; a longitude of 90° west signifies a time 6 hours behind Greenwich; and finally, a location which is almost 180° west of Greenwich has a time 12 hours behind that of Greenwich.

There is only one problem with all this, which can be seen from the following example. Suppose, say, it is 2 a.m. on a Sunday morning at Greenwich and we work out the times of other places on the earth. As we go eastward we finally reach a point on the meridian 180° from Greenwich which will be 12 hours ahead, and this will have a time of 2 p.m. on the Sunday. On the other hand as we go westward from Greenwich the time will drop further and further back until the point when we are almost on the meridian 180° west and the time will be 2 p.m. on the Saturday. Thus, we can reach a certain spot on the 180° meridian which would be 2 p.m. Sunday if we travelled to it eastward from Greenwich and 2 p.m. Saturday if we travelled to it westward from Greenwich. The time of the day would be the same but the day would be different. Thus the 180° meridian directly opposite the earth from the Greenwich meridian is called the International Date Line. If a 'plane or ship travelling eastward crosses this line the day suddenly changes back one—for example, from Sunday to Saturday, or from Friday to Thursday. On the other hand if the ship or aircraft is travelling westward and crosses the Date Line the day will suddenly make a jump of one day forward.

This gives rise to such interesting effects as a traveller being able to have two birthdays. If he crosses the International Date Line travelling eastward say at 2 a.m. on Sunday morning it will suddenly become 2 a.m. Saturday morning and he will have Saturday all over again. On the other hand a traveller crossing in the other direction will find 2 a.m. on a Saturday morning suddenly become 2 a.m. Sunday morning and he will appear to have missed the Saturday almost entirely.

Because it is inconvenient to have different cities and towns in the one State at different times, agreements have been reached

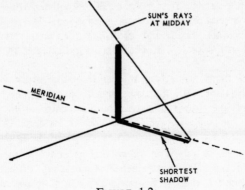

FIGURE 1.2

whereby the same time is observed within certain zones. For instance, people in eastern Australia observe Eastern Standard Time—which is an average of the true times throughout these areas and simply eliminates the possibility of having a whole series of different times throughout one State. This would create havoc with all time tables. The time in South Australia and the Northern Territory is taken as being half an hour behind Eastern Standard Time and in Perth, Western Australia, the time is taken as being two hours behind Eastern Standard Time. New Zealand time is two hours ahead of Eastern Standard Time.

Do you know how to determine the direction of the meridian or line of longitude at the place where you live? You can do this very easily. Recall that in Australia the sun always passes over to the north of us. Place a stick in the level ground and make sure it is vertical. On a sunny day keep marking the position of the end of its shadow. When the shadow is shortest it is midday or 12 noon. The line along the shortest shadow of the stick will always give you the north-south line, that is, the position of the meridian, as shown in *Figure 1.2*. You might try measuring the length of the shadow at noon each month during the year and note how it is shortest in mid-summer and longest in mid-winter.

It is, of course, true that knowing the longitude east or west of Greenwich of a given place does not tell you exactly where the place is on the earth's surface; it can be anywhere on a particular semi-circle extending from pole to pole. Another angle is required in order to completely specify a given point. This is called the *angle of latitude*. The latitude of Sydney, for example, is 34° south as shown in *Figure 1.1*. In effect this is measured in the following way:

Imagine firstly a line from the centre of the earth to that point on the Equator with the same longitude as Sydney; secondly, imagine a line drawn directly from the centre of the earth to Sydney. The angle between these lines is close to 34° and we say Sydney has a latitude close to 34° south of the Equator.

This angle as shown in *Figure 1.3* is equal to the angle of latitude of any place from which it is measured. As can be seen from *Figure 1.1*, there is a circle which can be drawn around the earth on which all points have a latitude of 34° south. The location of Sydney is, however, completely specified by saying that it has latitude 34° south and longitude 152° east. The location of Greenwich for example, is latitude 51° north and longitude 0°.

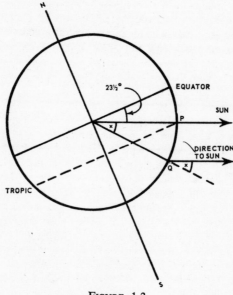

FIGURE 1.3

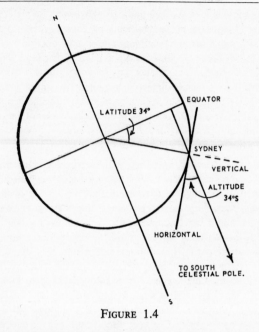

FIGURE 1.4

The latitude angle for a given place can be found by measuring the angle between the direct line to the sun and the vertical or horizontal provided one knows what season it is. Consider for example, the simple observation in *Figure 1.2.* From the length of the shortest shadow and the height of your stick you can determine the angle at which the sun's rays are reaching you. If, for example, you know that the date is December 21st, you know that the sun is directly over the Tropic of Capricorn—latitude $23\frac{1}{2}°$ south—and hence you can work out your own latitude. This is shown in *Figure 1.4.* An instrument has been devised called a sextant which enables an observer to measure the angle between the sun and the horizon and thereby determine his latitude.

In the early days of navigation sailors had considerable trouble in determining their positions. To locate themselves on the globe they had to determine both latitude and longitude. Once knowing the longitude—and the date—they could determine their latitude by methods such as we have just outlined. However, the determination of their longitude proved difficult for many years. For an accurate determination of longitude one needs accurate clocks. Consider, for example, a ship setting out from England with its clocks set at Greenwich time. After, say, several months of voyaging the longitude can be immediately determined by noting from the sun when it is 12 noon and seeing how many hours and minutes the clocks differ from 12 o'clock. Since each degree of longitude causes a time difference of four minutes the precise longitude east or west of Greenwich is thus known.

The difficulty, however, was that in the early days clocks could not be constructed accurately enough for good longitude determinations. This was so much of a problem that in 1714 a reward of £20,000 was offered by the British Government for any means of determining a ship's longitude accurate to within 30 nautical miles at the end of a six weeks' voyage—and this meant determining the longitude accurately to within about half a degree. The reward was won by John Harrison, a self-taught Yorkshire carpenter, who invented a marine time-keeper which fulfilled the conditions for the reward. You may realise what a step forward this was in the 18th century from the fact that a clock fulfilling the British Government's condition had to keep time accurately to better than 3 seconds per day—a standard which, at the time when the reward was offered, had not even been achieved by the best pendulum clocks on shore. The name *chronometer* was given to these accurate clocks for navigation, and today, of course, extremely accurate chronometers are used.

Over the ages man used various devices for indicating the regular passage of time during the day. The earliest mechanical clocks seemed to have been introduced in Europe during the 13th century and were used in churches to mark the times of services. A clock is said to have been erected, for example, at Westminster in 1288, and there is a clock actually remaining in England at Salisbury Cathedral which dates from 1386.

These early clocks all used gravity in some way to drive them. They employed a weight on the end of a strong line which would gradually be pulled downwards, by the earth's gravitational attraction. In the course of doing this the weight could operate the clock mechanism, and when the weight reached the bottom it would have to be wound up again.

An important development in clock construction was the introduction of the pendulum; its principle was first discovered by Galileo in 1581. The pendulum of a clock merely consists of an object or bob attached to the lower end of a light rod, the upper end of which is suspended from a support in such a manner that the rod and its bob are free to swing to and fro under the influence of gravity. The fact noted by Galileo is that the time for one complete to and fro swing of such a pendulum is almost completely independent of the magnitude of swing as long as this is not too large. Thus a swinging pendulum will have almost exactly the same time of swing whether oscillating through say 15° or 5°. The duration of swing of a pendulum varies with its length and a pendulum which makes one swing per second is slightly greater than 39 inches long.

The following story of how Galileo came to study the pendulum is told—and you shall be hearing more about it from Professor Julius Miller in his lectures. In 1581, at the age of 17 years, while kneeling in the Cathedral in Pisa, he observed the swinging of the Great Cathedral lamp, and, using his own pulse beat to measure the time, noted that the time of swing of the lamp was constant. He wrote afterwards: "Thousands of times I have observed vibrations, especially in churches, where lamps, suspended by long cords, had been inadvertently set into motion . . . But I never dreamed of learning . . . (that each) would employ the same time in passing . . ."

Thus Galileo discovered that a swinging pendulum would regularly "tick" away a unit of time—the period of swing—and that, even if the swing gradually died down, the period would remain unaffected. From this observation many types of pendulum clocks were developed based on the swinging pendulum, and in all of them only a very small amount of energy was needed to keep the pendulum swinging. A quite small weight attached to a string and being pulled down gradually by gravity was enough. Such pendulum clocks were much more accurate than previous types and many forms of pendulum clocks are still in existence today.

Nowadays, however, the pendulum can be kept swinging by means of a coiled spring.

In most small household clocks of today and in watches, the pendulum is replaced by an oscillating flywheel, while electric clocks simply use the oscillations of the alternating current mains supply as their regular unit of time.

Solar and Sidereal Time

We have said in the above that it is 12 noon for any observer when the sun passes most nearly overhead—that is, when the sun is vertically above his meridian—and that the time between the successive crossings of the sun over the same meridian is called a day—a *solar* day.

So far this sounds very simple. It appears an excellent way of measuring time. Scientifically, however, this definition of time has its problems, because the day defined in this way is not exactly constant; the solar day varies slightly in length throughout the year. We endeavour to make our clocks tick through 24 hours in what is the average time of a solar day.

You can very easily check for yourselves that the solar day is not quite constant by means of the following consideration: *Figure 1.5* is simply a diagram to illustrate what happens, for example, if there is a hole in a roof which permits a spot of sunlight to fall on the floor. If you can find such a situation you might be interested to mark where the spot of light occurs at 12 noon from day to day; you should take the time from an accurate clock or from the signals over a radio.

After you have kept such observations throughout a year you will have traced on the floor a figure eight with its long direction running north and south. The north-south movement of the spot of light is, of course, nothing to worry about; a meridian would run straight along the long axis of the figure eight, and if the spot did no more than move up and down this meridian with the changing season, it would mean that the sun was always crossing the meridian at the same time.

The east-west movement of the spot of sunlight, however, indicates that the sun is sometimes slightly ahead of our clocks and

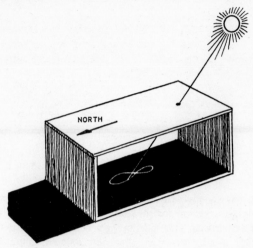

FIGURE 1.5

sometimes slightly behind them. Can you think of a reason for this?

One reason stems from the fact that the earth's orbit around the sun is not exactly circular—it is slightly elliptical. The earth's speed around this orbit changes slightly—when the earth is closest to the sun the speed is a maximum and when the earth is furthest away the speed is a minimum. Thus the distance travelled by the earth in its orbit in 24 hours changes slightly over the course of a year. The time taken for the earth's spin to point a certain meridian at the sun a second time is sometimes slightly in excess of 24 hours and sometimes slightly less. This effect of the earth's elliptical orbit, coupled with the tilt of the earth's axis of spin, produces the figure eight of *Figure 1.5*. The sun can sometimes be up to a quarter of an hour ahead of our clocks, and sometimes as much as a quarter of an hour behind them. This, of course, has little practical importance in our everyday living.

For scientific purposes, however, it can be of importance that we have a definition of a day which is not variable. All we have to do is to define a day as the interval of time between the transit of a star across the same meridian. This is called a sidereal day.

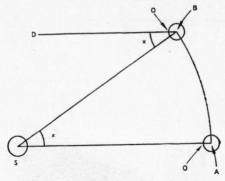

FIGURE 1.6

The solar day is approximately 4 minutes longer than the sidereal day, which is the reason for the fact that each night the stars rise 4 minutes earlier than they did the night before—according to our solar clocks. It is for this reason that any zodiacal constellation—together with the other stars—appears higher and higher in the night sky as the seasons progress, and completes a cycle in one year.

We can actually calculate how this 4-minute difference arises. Let us suppose that in one day the earth moves from A to B through an angle x—as shown in *Figure 1.6*. Since the year is about 365 days long, the angle x is 360/365°, or approximately 1°. When the earth is at A the sun is seen by an observer at 0 along the line AS. When the earth is at B and has made one complete turn through 360 degrees the observer is again at position 0. However, now it is not 12 noon for him because the vertical direction from his meridian is now BD which does not point at the sun. He must wait until the earth spins through a further angle $x = 1°$ in order that it is 12 noon, and as we saw previously this corresponds to 4 minutes of time.

In the case of sidereal time, you should imagine the sun in *Figure 1.6* to be turned into a star and moved millions of times further away to the left. Clearly the line BD will still essentially point directly to the star. This is why it is that the sidereal day is the day which really measures the time taken for the earth to revolve through 360 degrees.

While the sidereal day is thus a more satisfactory definition scientifically, you will appreciate that for practical reasons we must set our ordinary clocks to keep step as closely as possible with the sun, so that our 24-hour day is then an average or mean solar day.

Space and Time

Thus time on earth ticks on. Is this the full meaning of time—the fact that we can use the behaviour of the earth, and of artificial devices which we have constructed for regulating our lives? Surely not. We are but living beings on one single planet in the entire universe. The universe is not static. Innumerable changes are continuously occurring within it, changes which are completely unaffected by our existence. New suns are in the process of formation, old suns are "dying", new galaxies are being formed—things are happening with the passage of time in the universe.

It is clear that in any discussion of the universe in general the concept of space—that is, the distance between objects in the universe—is far from sufficient. One must also consider the behaviour of the universe as regards time. It will be our task in the remaining chapters to give an elementary introduction to the concept of time in the universe, and to this end we devote the next chapter to building up a picture of how the universe appears to us and of where we, and our solar system, stand in relation to it.

CHAPTER 2

The Universe

The Solar System

The things that seem normal to us and to which we are accustomed, are things on earth because, after all, that is where we live; while what happens to us on earth is certainly important, we are in fact a tiny speck in the universe.

For instance, our earth is only a satellite of the sun, which is a tremendously hot object nearly one million miles in diameter. The sun produces its heat and light by hydrogen bomb reactions deep in its central region. This has been going on for several thousand million years. Yet there is still so much matter in the sun that it will continue exploding and producing heat for at least several thousand million more years. This great object has a number of satellites—planets—revolving around it, one of which is Earth.

The closest planet to the sun is Mercury, circling about 36 million miles from the sun; then come Venus, Earth—circling about 93 million miles from the sun—Mars, Jupiter, Saturn, Uranus, Neptune

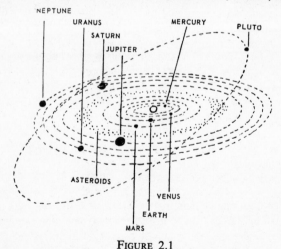

FIGURE 2.1

The solar system. Neither the distances nor the angles shown are to scale.

27

and finally the outermost planet, Pluto, which travels in its orbit at an average distance of 3,700 million miles from the sun. Most of you would have seen a diagram of the solar system such as that in *Figure 2.1*. The relative sizes of the different planets are shown in *Figure 2.2*.

Many planets have their own satellites or moons revolving around them. Our own earth has one moon, other planets have several moons and only a few have none. The sun and its planets, and these planets with their moons, we call our *solar system*.

You have only to look at the sky on a clear night to realise that this solar system is not the entire universe. It is in fact merely a small speck in that part of the universe which we can see. Nearly all the myriads of heavenly bodies which we see in the sky are other suns, millions upon millions of miles away. The only exceptions to this are the planets which, by reflecting sunlight, appear like stars to us.

Galaxies

It is probable that about half of these other suns also have their own planets revolving around them. In other words, many of the stars that we see in the sky are centres of other solar systems, each consisting of a separate sun with planets revolving around it. The nearest star to us which can be seen by the naked eye is the brighter of the two pointers of the Southern Cross, and this is so far away that light from it takes four and a half years to reach us. Light travels at 186,000 miles per second, and so you may work out that the distance to this star is about 27 million million miles.

But even distant stars which we can see with the naked eye when we look at the sky on a clear night are still nowhere near the limits of the universe. When scientists look at the heavens through large telescopes they see that our sun is but one of a large group of suns which we call a *galaxy*. There are in fact something like 100,000 million suns in this group or cluster of suns which we call our galaxy. We can also tell that all these suns in our galaxy are formed into a pattern so that the overall shape of the galaxy is flat but with a bulging centre—something like a fried egg hanging in space. So large is our group of suns—our galaxy—that it takes light about a hundred thousand years to go right across it,

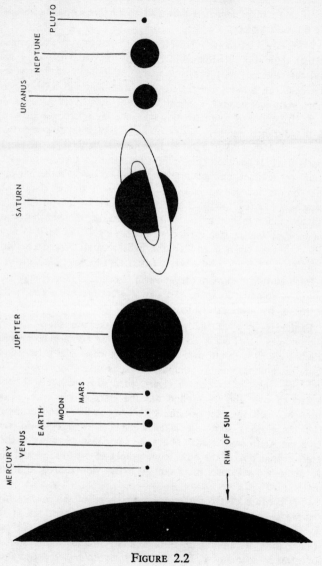

FIGURE 2.2

and it even takes light ten thousand years to go straight through the narrowest parts.

With large telescopes, however, it is possible to look much further than this. Astronomers can look beyond our galaxy and find that there is mostly empty space for millions of light years. Scientists call a *light year* the distance that light will travel in one year; you may readily confirm that one light year is close to 6×10^{12} miles. Eventually, however, the big telescopes show up in the distance another cluster of stars somewhat like our own galaxy; and then after another few million light years of empty space there is another cluster of stars, and at greater distances again, yet another, and again another, and so on. So the universe goes on as far as we can see—which with today's largest of telescopes is a few thousand million light years or several thousand million million million miles. It is an interesting thought that when we look at such a star cluster we are seeing it not as it is now, but as it was when it emitted the light several thousand million years ago. Looking a long way away is also looking back in time.

Each cluster of stars in the universe is called a galaxy, and each galaxy is spinning in space just like a great catherine-wheel; this is true of our own galaxy too.

Examples of what the galaxies look like are shown in the photographs. In *Figure 2.3*, for example, we see a galaxy which is relatively close to our own, called Andromeda. This great galaxy contains millions upon millions of suns like our own. The catherine-wheel effect can be clearly seen; the small bright spots dotted all over the foreground are the stars of our own galaxy through which our telescope must look to see the distant galaxies. The big glowing spots are smaller galaxies of a type different from the Andromeda galaxy about the same distance away as their large companion. In the other photographs of *Figures 2.4* and *2.5*, we see other examples of distant galaxies, viewed from different angles.

It is because of the catherine-wheel shape of our own galaxy that we see what we call the *Milky Way*. When we look at the sky in such a direction that we are looking through the flat part of our galaxy, we are looking through a large number of the stars of our galaxy—so many in fact that they give a milky appearance.

The Great Nebula in Andromeda—a system of some 10,000,000,000 stars, similar to our own galaxy. It is the nearest of the other great systems, yet its light takes over a million years to reach us. This photograph was taken with a 24-in. reflecting telescope.
(Yerkes Observatory)

FIGURE 2.3
The Andromeda galaxy.

FIGURE 2.4
A spiral galaxy, showing the swirling "Catherine-wheel" effect.

FIGURE 2.5
We are looking side-on at this distant galaxy.

This is the Milky Way, which is thickest when we are looking towards the centre of our galaxy. However, when we look in a direction which leads very quickly out of the galaxy, for example, at right-angles to the flat plane, we do not see anything like as many stars and therefore do not see a milky appearance.

Each of the galaxies in the universe contains from 100 million to 100,000 million stars. As already mentioned, large numbers of these stars or suns probably have planets revolving around them; and on each of these planets there is some chance of life existing. What an insignificant fraction of all the life in the universe we may form! Scientists estimate that, even within our own galaxy which is itself such a speck in the universe, there are possibly 50,000 million suns with planets revolving around them.

Gravitational Fields

All the heavenly bodies of the universe seem to be moving in near-circular tracks. Our moon moves in a near-circular orbit around the earth; artificial satellites may also move in almost circular orbits around the earth, and the other planets move in orbits that are nearly circular around the sun. Then again galaxies of millions upon millions of suns turn in space like huge catherine-wheels. Why is this so?

One of the most famous and far-reaching laws of nature, which was first realised by Sir Isaac Newton in the seventeenth century, is called *Newton's Law of Universal Gravitation;* Newton realised that the only way of understanding many observations on the behaviour of objects in our solar system was to assume that any object automatically attracts any other object. This is called the *force of gravitation.* We, as objects on this earth, are attracted by the earth and pulled towards its centre. This gives us our weight. If some object is freed some distance away from the earth it is pulled towards the earth by the gravitational forces. To us the object falls.

It was Newton himself who realised that earth satellites might come to be. *Figure 2.6* shows a diagram similar to one which Newton drew, in which we have an imaginary mountain sticking hundreds of miles up right through the atmosphere. In his little fairy-tale experiment, Newton imagined a cannon being fired from the top of this mountain. The faster the cannon ball is fired the further it will fall away from the base of the mountain.

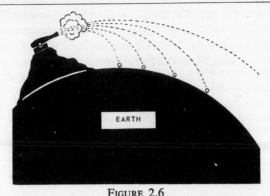

FIGURE 2.6

Newton's diagram to illustrate the principle of earth satellites.

Eventually, if fired fast enough, it will travel so far sideways while falling that the earth's surface falls away underneath it at the same rate. Although falling continuously the cannon ball will never hit the earth's surface and will in fact be an earth satellite. The cannon ball would have to be fired at about 17,500 miles per hour; this is the *minimum* speed at which earth satellites must be fired. Of course, nowadays Newton's mountain is replaced by modern rockets which take satellites up to high altitudes and fire them sideways into satellite orbits.

It may thus be clear to you why satellites must orbit the earth in near-circular orbits. There can never be a satellite which is standing still in space several hundred miles away from the earth, because it would be drawn towards the earth by the gravitational pull and crash on the earth's surface. If an object is going to remain in space near the earth it will have to be moving around the earth all the time; although being under the action of the gravitational pull and falling all the time, its sideways movement keeps carrying it fast enough so that the earth's surface falls away underneath all the time. Our moon similarly makes a complete circuit around the earth once in a little over 27 days, and is thus a satellite of the earth.

The earth in turn is a satellite of the sun. We could never lead a nice comfortable life 93 million miles away from the sun unless we were moving around it. If we were not moving sideways around the sun we would be drawn straight in towards it and would crash through its fiery surface within a matter of a few days. This disaster is avoided only because the earth is travelling around the sun at about 65,000 miles per hour, which is what is required for it to be a satellite of the sun. The other planets also are moving around the sun at speeds which keep them in their orbits. The planet Mars, for example, makes one complete revolution around the sun in 687 days; the Martian year is thus almost twice as long as our year. On the other hand Venus, which is closer to the sun than we are, makes one complete revolution in about eight earth months.

If all the suns of the galaxies were still, they would be drawn together by their gravitational attraction for each other and eventually collide. The continual movement of galaxies, whirling like giant catherine-wheels, prevents them from collapsing into a huge central star.

You can thus realise what a major influence this force of gravity has in our universe. We live continually under the gravitational influence of our earth which gives us our weight. In science we say we live in the earth's gravitational field. Similarly, the earth and everything on it is moving under the influence of the sun's gravitational field. Then again our sun and its planets are moving in a giant circle under the influence of the gravitational field of our galaxy—the assembly of some 100,000 million suns.

Time Scale of the Solar System

Within the scope of these lectures it is not appropriate that we should go into great detail about modern theories of the formation of our solar system. Suffice it to say that it is considered to have formed from a large nebulous cloud of slowly rotating gas which has contracted and condensed into the solar system over millions of years.

The central part of the solar system is the sun itself and it is almost certain that many other stars of our galaxy also have planetary systems which have been formed by the same type of process. When gases contract to form a star, the young star consists mainly of fundamental atomic particles—that is, protons and electrons and a relatively small number of other nuclei. As the sun contracts under its own gravitational forces it "heats up" and so violent are collisions between the atomic particles or nuclei that nuclear reactions can take place with release of energy—the source of all the radiation from the sun.

With our present understanding of nuclear processes it is possible to calculate what we believe must be going on within stars, and it is found that each star must have a "lifetime". As the original light elements such as hydrogen are used up in the nuclear reactions and more and more heavier elements are manufactured, the star may even blow apart eventually. This occurs when the amount of energy being released in the nuclear reactions becomes so great that the internal gravitational forces can no longer hold the star together.

Such an occurrence was actually observed from earth in the year 1054, when a certain star suddenly began to glow with amazing brilliance. Night after night it grew brighter and to those who watched it, it appeared to be expanding. Eventually it started to dim and gradually disappeared from view. A star had "died".

The description of this event has been found in Chinese writings. Large telescopes, pointed to the spot where the star appeared, show what remains; it is called the "Crab Nebula" and represents the remnants of the star distributed in a great gaseous cloud and still expanding outwards rapidly. Such an explosion of a star—called a *super nova*—occurs in our galaxy about once every fifty years on the average. After such an explosion, nuclei of the various elements which were formed in the star are scattered across millions of miles of space. This may well be the fate of our own sun eventually. It has used up about half of its original supply of hydrogen, but this has already taken several thousand million years. Our sun is in the equilibrium stage where it still has ample hydrogen left and is radiating energy into space at the same rate as it is being released within it; thus the sun will probably last for a few thousand million more years.

We thus see that from observations of the sun, and from calculations regarding the nuclear reactions proceeding within it, we estimate that our solar system must have an age of several thousand million years

Geologists also contribute significantly to age estimates. If the earth originated as a hot gas or liquid and cooled to a solid it must have been continually losing heat. If the amount of heat being lost each year could be determined it should then be possible to calculate how long ago it would have been a liquid or a gas.

It is well-known that the temperature within the earth rises with depth below the surface; indeed in some mines over a mile deep, cold air has to be brought in to enable men to work. This enables approximate calculations to be made of the annual loss of heat from the earth. In 1883 Lord Kelvin, using the figures obtained for this loss of heat, calculated that the earth could not be more than 400 million years old but he later believed that the age was nearer to 20 million.

Geologists, on the other hand, by means of their study of the earth's crust, believed that the earth must be over a thousand million years old. The theoretical estimates such as made by Kelvin have now been brought into line with the geologists' estimates as it is now known that heat is continually being supplied within the earth by radio-active minerals. This means, of course, that Kelvin's original figure was based on an incorrect premise.

The discovery of radio-activity has, however, led to a very accurate method—called radio-active dating—for determining the age of the earth. The results from a variety of radio-active methods all yield an age in the vicinity of $4\frac{1}{2}$ thousand million years.

Astronomical and Biological Time

We thus see that time and space in the universe are incredibly large; we cannot really grasp the limits of them if indeed there are any. It is particularly impressive just how short a length of time such as a million years is as far as the universe is concerned; yet to us, of course, a million years seems like eternity. This just emphasizes that there are really two essentially different concepts of time. The first is what we might call *biological time* and which is the impression most of us automatically have as regards time. To us a hundred years is a fairly long time because it is in general more than one lifetime. A thousand years is a very long time and looking back 1,000 years takes us well back into history to the time of the Battle of Hastings, for example. A few thousand years and we are back into really ancient history, and with a million years we are back almost to the first evidence of man-like beings on earth. Yet to the universe, and even just to our own solar system and the earth itself, a million years is nothing; it is a tiny fraction of time in the history of the solar system.

Thus there is another concept of time which we might call *astronomical time* which applies to the universe. Great galaxies can form and stars develop, individual stars go through a "life cycle" and "die" and so the contents of the universe keep on changing. Yet the normal life span of a sun is several thousand million years.

It may have been surprising for you to realise that our own sun is thought to be "middle-aged" and that it will have burnt through all its nuclear reactions—reactions involving the nuclei of atoms— within a few thousand million years, at which time our entire solar system could well disintegrate into individual atomic particles. Does this worry us? Not at all, because a few thousand million years into the future is something that we cannot even contemplate. Our race will probably long since have become extinct, and to us even the future of a thousand years times is very uncertain.

One way of appreciating these two concepts of time, the biological and the astronomical, is the following: consider a large book such as a volume of the *Encyclopaedia Britannica* and let us imagine that it has one thousand pages and that it contains simply a history of the earth from its origin to the present day. Suppose, moreover, that the book is so composed that equal periods of time are given the same amount of space. Since there are 1,000 pages this would mean that every 20 pages would have to cover a period of about one hundred million years. Now we cannot tell exactly when life started on earth, but the earliest forms for which evidence has been found, existed about one thousand million years ago. Thus it is only the last 200 pages or so that would relate to the whole development of life on earth; the first 800 pages would provide very interesting reading indeed because it would all relate to the earlier development of the solar system and earth about which we can really only theorise.

The last 200 pages of the book would deal with the evolution of life on earth leading finally to the appearance of man. However, the final 20 pages would have to deal with the last one hundred million years and it would only be in about the last paragraph or two that the first indication of early man would appear. In the way this book would be arranged *the final line would cover roughly the last 80,000 years* and the final word would have to cover about *the last 5,000 years*. What about our present era? If by this we mean the history of the last century we would have no chance of finding it at all; it would represent a tiny portion of the last full-stop in the book.

Age of the Universe

In the above we have discussed the age of our sun and our solar system. On the basis of observation and calculation the natural life span of a typical sun would appear to be of the order of 10 thousand million years or 10^{10} years.

But just as the average life span of a typical human being says nothing about the age of mankind in general, so the average life span of a sun says nothing about the age of the universe. Although each person today may have an average life expectancy of a little over 70 years, this has no bearing on the time over which man has inhabited the earth.

In the next two chapters we shall consider the tremendously interesting issues raised when we ask the question: "How old is the universe?"

CHAPTER 3

Hubble's Time Constant

Olbers' Paradox

In 1826 a German astronomer, Heinrich Olbers, published a remarkable paper in which he arrived at a famous paradox regarding the universe. Although it was not realised at the time the most plausible solution to Olbers' paradox would, over a hundred years ago, already have led scientists to the conclusion that *the universe is expanding.*

Olbers performed an extremely simple calculation. We all know that the sky is black, or at least extremely dark, at night except for the close visible stars of our own galaxy. Olbers simply estimated the total amount of light which should reach us from all the stars and distant galaxies.

The calculation depended on the simple assumption that the distribution of galaxies throughout the universe is on the average uniform, that is, the average density of galaxies in the universe is uniform. This simply means that we assume that any large volume—say $(10^8$ light years$)^3$—contains the same number of galaxies.

Although galaxies differ one from another we can, for simplicity, assume that the universe is made up of "typical" galaxies all of which emit the same amount of radiation—say E in appropriate units of energy per unit time.

Now let us consider *Figure 3.1* in which we draw a spherical shell around the earth imagined to be at 0. The radius of this shell is R in some appropriate units of length, and the thickness is d. Then the volume of this shell is $4\pi R^2 d$ as long as the thickness d is much less than the radius R; the number of galaxies in the shell is thus $4\pi R^2 d \times n$ where n is the average number of galaxies in unit volume (unit volume being defined in terms of whatever unit of length we have chosen).

What energy is reaching us from these distant galaxies within the shell? We know that if the total energy being radiated by a single galaxy is E then the energy falling per unit time on unit area a distance R away is $E/4\pi R^2$. The intensity of the radiant

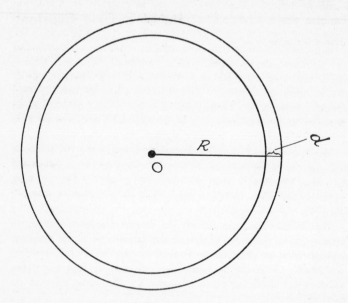

FIGURE 3.1

energy at 0 from the total number of galaxies in the spherical shell must thus be proportional to $4\pi R^2 d\ n\ \times\ E/4\pi R^2 = E\ n\ d$.

The important result here is that this is independent of the radius R of the shell. To calculate the total intensity of radiant energy at the earth's surface from distant galaxies we must add up the contributions from all such shells, and if the universe is of infinite extent *our answer would be itself infinite*.

Naturally a correction has to be made to this first result because the light from very distant galaxies has some chance of being blocked or intercepted by closer galaxies. When this correction is applied, the answer obtained is still very surprising. It is that the intensity of radiation at any point in the universe must be precisely the same as on the surface of a typical star or sun.

This is obviously not the case as the surface of the earth is obviously not at 6,000° C. or so, characteristic of the surface of the sun. The result is clearly absurd. Yet it is not that Olbers made an absurd calculation, for the assumption of a uniform universe was a very straightforward one and the result followed simply and logically from this. Olbers himself tried to resolve the paradox by postulating that there must be some form of continuous gas between galaxies which gradually absorbs radiation travelling over very long distances and which could not be detected by astronomical observations. This attempted explanation was not tenable, however, as even if this gas existed it would reach an equilibrium temperature such that it radiates as much energy as it receives and no longer acts as an absorber.

One interesting way out of the paradox occurs when one realises that, on the Olbers calculation, one-half of the enormous calculated radiation intensity at the earth's surface would be coming from galaxies more than 10^{20} light years away. Suppose, therefore, that the universe is "very young" and that it only started "operating" a relatively short time ago. If the galaxies were distributed through space as they are now but were somehow "turned on" at some time in the past, then the radiation from very distant ones would not have yet had time to reach us. If indeed the stars of the galaxies did not start to radiate until some moment in universe history, the darkness of our night sky tells us that this would have had to be somewhere between 10^8 and 10^{12} years ago.

For in this case any galaxies further away than this would have radiation on its way to us but not as yet having reached us. On this explanation the night sky would gradually, over the hundreds of millions of years, be becoming brighter and brighter as more and more radiation arrived and eventually the earth would "fry".

It is to be noticed, however, that the time of "switching on" of the stars of the universe in this explanation would be remarkably "recent" in history. The lower estimate of 10^8 years can be ruled out simply on the basis that we know the earth is older than this, although the upper limit of 10^{12} years would be permissible on these grounds.

We now know, however, that no such *ad hoc* switching on process for the universe is needed to resolve Olbers' paradox. One solution which was not considered by Olbers was discovered by direct astronomical observation in the present century: *the universe is expanding*.

When spectroscopic photographs are taken of the light from distant galaxies it is observed that there is a *Doppler Shift* of the light. Any characteristic spectral line from a known element on a distant galaxy appears to us to have a lower frequency which is simply a doppler effect due to the fact that the galaxy is moving away from us.

In later chapters of this book you will see how the doppler effect for light is calculated. Suffice it to say here, however, that the energy carried by radiation decreases with decreasing frequency.

The astronomical observation shows that the further a galaxy is away from us, the faster away it is moving. When one goes to the extreme, distant galaxies such as enter in the Olbers' calculation, one reaches the situation when wave-lengths in the visible region reach us way down in, say, the infra-red or even radio region. Thus it is quite understandable that the night sky is dark simply because of the doppler change in characteristics of the radiation reaching us from the distant galaxies. No longer is the total energy reaching us from a distant spherical shell independent of the radius of that shell because the larger the radius the faster are the galaxies within it moving away and the less the energy reaching us.

It is an extremely interesting concept, however, that our night sky is dark, and that the surface of the earth is not at something like 6,000° C., and in fact that the earth and the life on it can exist, only because distant galaxies are behaving in a certain way. In this sense our existence is dependent on what is happening to galaxies even more than 10^{20} light years away.

The Law of Expansion

By now, detailed observations of the "red shift"—that is, the doppler effect—of a large number of distant galaxies have been performed and a simple law for the expansion of the universe deduced.

This simple law is based on what is called the *cosmological principle* in which it is assumed that the expansion of the universe is going on everywhere and that it would appear to be expanding in the same way from each point in the universe. We on earth see all distant galaxies moving away from us, but suppose we were on a planet in some distant galaxy say 10^{12} light years away. The cosmological principle assumes that we would still see all other galaxies moving away from us by the same law as we would derive here on earth.

This is not a very difficult concept to appreciate as can be seen by a one-dimensional analogy. Suppose we consider a piece of elastic which is being stretched at a uniform rate. If initially there were marks along the elastic say one inch apart (imagine the elastic to be initially several feet long) then as the elastic is stretched so each mark gets further away from its neighbours. Any "observer" situated at one of the marks would see the nearest marks on either side getting further away, the next nearest marks on either side moving away more rapidly, and so on. It is this same picture in three-dimensions that we imagine within the expanding universe.

On this picture the velocity V of movement away from us of an object of distance R as given by the simple law is

$$V = R/T$$

where T is some constant of the universe with the dimensions of time.

The evaluation of this constant T depends on detailed astronomical measurements not only of the doppler effects of distant galaxies (which determine V) but also on measurements of their distances away (to determine R). The distance estimates are by far the more difficult to obtain accurately. In his book, *The Realm of the Nebulae* published in 1936, the astronomer E. P. Hubble summarised observations up to that time and gave a figure for T of 1.8×10^9 years. This value was accepted for many years until the great astronomer Baade showed in 1952 that the distance measurements had previously been seriously underestimated and that the true value for T was considerably greater. The current value of T which is widely accepted as being reliable is $T = 1.3 \times 10^{10}$ years.

The significance of this "time constant" of the universe may be realised if we assume that the distant galaxies are moving away from us at uniform speed and are not being accelerated. For then we can project back into the past to see how close galaxies were together at various stages in history. On carrying this to the limit we find that all the galaxies of the universe must have been accumulated into a small region 1.3×10^{10} years ago. The whole behaviour of the universe would then appear as if an explosion or "big bang" had taken place in this concentrated space 1.3×10^{10} years ago and that the material of the universe started flying apart. Over the ensuing millions of years the faster moving matter would cover greater distances than the more slowly moving fragments leading to an expanding universe consistent with what is presently observed.

Should we say therefore that 1.3×10^{10} years is the age of the universe? It seems surprisingly short when we consider that the lifetime of a typical sun is about 10^{10} years, and on all plausible arguments for how galaxies have accumulated and formed we arrive at necessary time scales greater than this. Even within our own galaxy we can see stars that are old and which have run through their life cycle, as well as others which have finally reached an explosive *super nova* stage. We would like to imagine that our own galaxy has had more time to evolve in peace than would have been granted it by a "big bang" 1.3×10^{10} years ago.

Some scientists do indeed believe that the Hubble constant T should be taken to be the "age of the universe" and that everything started with a "big bang" at some such time in the distant past. Yet in the next chapter we shall see that this is not a necessary conclusion and that the universe is perhaps even of "infinite age", and that the question *"how old is the universe?"* is therefore meaningless.

CHAPTER 4

Space and Time

Mach's Principle

In this chapter we shall see that the concept of time is not simply a useful and interesting one which we use to regulate our lives and in terms of which we can discuss the history of the earth or speculate on the age of the universe but it is one of the most fundamental concepts in physics.

At this stage we shall discuss something which seems to have no bearing whatsoever on our main topic "Time in the Universe": the question as to why objects have *mass*. Yet we shall see that there is a very real connection indeed.

Newton's laws of motion are familiar to all who have had even the mildest introduction to physics. The idea or the notion that "an object remains at rest or continues to move with uniform velocity unless acted upon by an external force" becomes almost second nature to all science students. Then again the fact that when a force acts on an object it produces an acceleration according to the famous law $F = m\,a$ is one of the basic equations of mechanics. The quantity m, of course, is the *mass* of the object.

There is one aspect of Newtonian mechanics, however, which is far from obvious and raises such deep questions that it is rarely discussed in normal physics courses. This is, that Newton's laws are really true only under certain special circumstances.

Imagine, for example, a time in the not-too-distant future when communication satellites will be orbiting the earth in so-called "stationary orbits". A stationary orbit is an equatorial orbit at a height of about 22,000 miles for which the period of rotation of the satellite is exactly 24 hours. Thus, in the ideal orbit, the satellite would always remain above the same spot on the equator because the earth also is revolving once in every 24 hours.

Imagine someone (whom we shall call an observer) being at this point and "observing" the satellite with whatever scientific apparatus he needs for the purpose. He is not interested in the sun or the distant stars but simply in the satellite itself. *To him the satellite is stationary.* Yet he knows that a gravitational force is acting upon it directly towards the earth. Thus from his observations he would say that although there is a force acting on the satellite it is stationary. To be consistent with Newton's second law our observer would have to say that there must be another force acting on the satellite apart from gravity—which he might call a centrifugal force—which acts upwards and exactly balances the gravitational force.

On the other hand we imagine our observer looking at the earth and its satellite from afar—such as we are imagining ourselves to be when we look at *Figure 2.6* for example—everything checks nicely. The satellite indeed always has an acceleration towards the centre of the earth which accounts for it continually "falling" and it is simply because of its uniform sideways speed that it remains in orbit. Newton's law applies without modification and force is proportional to acceleration, the constant of proportionality being the mass of the satellite.

Thus it depends what type of "observer" you are as to whether you can employ Newton's second law directly or whether you have to imagine other forces being introduced to make it work. Our observer on the earth, watching the stationary satellite, has to conclude that there is an equal and opposite force to the gravitational force acting on the satellite; such forces which must be introduced to make Newton's second law apply are called *inertial forces.*

What is the difference between the two observers, the one on the earth looking at the "stationary" satellite and the other imagined to be looking at the earth satellite system from afar? The student may say that the answer is obvious and that the observer on the earth, rotating with the earth, is being accelerated. But the observer on the earth may choose to regard himself as stationary and to be a perfectly valid observer. What is it then that determines the type of observer for whom Newton's laws apply without the introduction of inertial forces to make them work?

This is a question which Newton himself wondered about and which has occupied the attention of philosophers and scientists ever since Newton's day. The great Viennese physicist and philosopher Ernst Mach (1838-1916) devoted a tremendous amount of attention to this question and was responsible for a line of thought which profoundly influenced Albert Einstein in all his work. Mach observed that one difference between two observers such as we have quoted above is that the one on the earth would see the distant stars moving across the heavens; in other words, the distant stars to the observer on earth would appear to be rotating around the earth.

Thus it would appear that Newton's second law applies directly if the observer is in a frame of reference in which the distant stars appear not to be moving. This led Mach to suggest that the distant stars and galaxies in the universe must somehow be exerting an influence on the laws of mechanics here on earth. Just as our sky is dark because of properties of the distant galaxies, so perhaps the entire framework of mechanics as we know it, with objects having inertial mass and moving under the influence of forces according to Newton's laws, is determined in some manner by an influence from the far-reaching galaxies of the universe. Otherwise it would appear strange that the frames of reference—called *inertial frames*—in which Newton's laws work without introduction of inertial forces—can only be defined in connection with the distant stars.

Mach's suggestion at first aroused tremendous criticism. Bertrand Russell for example, wrote in 1927—11 years after Mach's death— that ". . . the influence attributed to the fixed stars savours of astrology, and is scientifically incredible." Similarly A. N. Whitehead, in 1920, made the remark that "it is difficult to take seriously the suggestion that these domestic phenomena on the earth are due to the influence of the fixed stars. I cannot persuade myself to believe that a little star in its twinkling turned round Foucault's pendulum in the Paris Exhibition of 1851."

The summary of Mach's philosophy was that inertial frames are those which are unaccelerated relative to what he called the "fixed stars", which today can be interpreted as relative to some average of all the matter in the universe. Moreover according to Mach, matter has inertia only because there is other matter in the universe. Einstein was so impressed with these statements that he called them "Mach's Principle".

How could distant matter of the universe determine the laws of mechanics here on earth or, for that matter, anywhere else in the universe? This question certainly has not been definitely answered today, but it is realised that there is the distinct possibility that this may be so. Dr. D. W. Sciama of Cambridge University has, in fact, produced a recent theory in this regard. Sciama does not say that his theory must necessarily be correct, but it is developed simply as an example to show how the very property which we call the inertial mass of an object may be determined by all the other matter of the universe.

Sciama's theory can best be discussed qualitatively by analogy first to the field of electricity. You know that any two electric charges exert a force on each other; in fact around any electric charge there is a field of influence which moves outward from the charge at the speed of light. As you may learn in your later studies of electricity and magnetism that the entire field of what we call magnetism is due to the fact that a moving electric charge is sending out its influence at the speed of light, such that a second charge is feeling the influence of the first with a "time lag" due to the finite speed with which the influence is propagated between them. (We discussed this matter at some length in our last year's Summer School Lecture. It is not our purpose here to discuss in detail the subject of electro-magnetism, but it is true to say that the finite speed of propagation of electrical influences is the basis of a complete understanding of all magnetic effects and the generation of electro-magnetic radiation itself.)

In the same way we say there is a gravitational field of influence, around any object in the universe, which is believed also to propagate with the speed of light. Sciama assumes that precisely the same sort of phenomena occur with gravitational influences as in the case of electric fields. On this basis he is able to show that an object at rest or moving with uniform velocity relative to the "matter average" of the universe would continue to do so and thereby satisfy Newton's first law. Similarly any attempt to accelerate it relative to the "matter average" would meet an "inertial resistance" in just the way required by Newton's second law. Thus what we call the inertial mass of an object would be a property not only of the object itself but of the universe as a whole. In fact on the Sciama theory, 80 per cent of the contribution to an object's mass would be from the influence of distant galaxies further away than can be detected by the giant 200 inch telescope at Mount Palomar.

If such an idea is correct it is clear how the inertial frames, in which Newton's law apply, are to be defined—by the simple statement of Mach's Principle.

It is also clear that the constant of proportionality in Newton's second law, the quantity that we call the inertial mass of an object, is due to the gravitational influence of all the distant objects in the universe. If the object is at rest or moving uniformly in the "matter average" frame of reference of the universe, the total sum of all the gravitational forces from the universe at large is zero; with the universe spreading on the average symmetrically in all directions away from the object, all the individual contributions to the gravitational effect exactly cancel and there is nothing to modify the motion. Once a force acts on the object and begins to accelerate it, the sum total of the distant gravitational influences gives it an inertia, or the property that has been called inertial mass.

Changing Time Scale

We have seen in the previous chapter that the universe is expanding. We would therefore expect that in another thousand million years for example, the distant galaxies will be further away from us than they are now—in other words, that the universe will be of "lower density". If the inertial mass of any object is determined by all the other matter in the universe, it is natural to expect on the above picture that the masses of objects will gradually be changing. This may mean that the rate of passage of time is also gradually changing. We measure the passage of time by means of what we call clocks. Any repetitive device such as an orbit described under gravity or something that oscillates regularly can be used as a clock. It is however impossible to compare intervals of time which occur at completely different periods in the universe's history so that we cannot automatically say for example, that time must be "flowing uniformly".

It may be that *dynamical* clocks, such as those which employ the period of motion of a planet in orbit, are ever so gradually changing their rates due to changing masses.

On the other hand we also have so-called *atomic clocks,* which are dependent on the fundamental periods associated with the movement of electrons within atoms and molecules. If masses are gradually changing, what about the electric charges of electrons and protons? The fundamental unit of an electric charge—the charge of an electron—is something entirely different from mass. Thus with the passage of time, atomic clocks may be changing their rates quite differently from dynamical clocks. If a dynamical and atomic clock are in perfect synchronism today, it could be that in a thousand million years' time, the seconds or minutes which each ticks away will be quite different.

In an expanding universe it may thus not be so at all, that time-wise, everything scales in the same way. It could be, for example, that 10^{10} years ago the universe was, as it were, much more "wound up" so that much more action occurred in what we now call one second; it may also be that, in this sense, the universe is gradually "winding down". All this, however, is mere speculation; the definite point to be made is that inertial masses may be gradually changing and that one cannot automatically think of "a uniform flow of time".

Steady State Theory

With our knowledge that the distant galaxies are moving away from us and that the universe is expanding, it seems that we cannot escape the conclusion that the universe is changing with time. The rate of passage of time itself may be changing in a manner which is "tied in" with the overall changing of the universe. It seems at first sight that something like the "big bang" theory of the universe is inescapable.

In such a theory, of course, nothing can be said at all about how all the matter of the universe was originally created. This thought provided the motivation for a recent very ingenius theory regarding the universe proposed by Hoyle, Bondi and Gold. (Both Professors Bondi and Gold are lecturing in the present series and you shall be hearing from them directly.) Briefly, the basis of this so-called "Steady State" theory is that, if we must assume that matter was somehow created anyway, why not assume that it is going on continuously? Detailed calculations show that if one neutron or hydrogen atom "popped into existence" so rarely that it need occur in one litre of space only once in 5×10^{11} years, this would be enough to keep the density of the universe constant.

As existing galaxies draw further apart over the thousands of millions of years, so new matter would gradually come together and, under the action of gravitational forces, new galaxies would continually be forming. In this way the average distance between galaxies throughout all time would remain constant even though galaxies themselves are being formed, go through an evolutionary period, grow old and gradually become "dormant".

Philosophically this theory has considerable attraction as it would mean that the universe would, on the average, be remaining constant. The cosmological principle would apply not only to space but also to time. An "observer" located anywhere in the universe and at any time would automatically see the same sort of universe around him. He would always see distant galaxies moving away from him but the average distance between galaxies would always be the same. How the matter comes into existence is, of course, far beyond our understanding by any present laws of science; yet it requires no more of an assumption than to say that all the matter of the universe was suddenly created at some time in the distant past, because we equally well have no means of knowing how that could have occurred.

An advantage of this theory is that at least it can be tested by observation.

As new telescopes and radio telescopes are being built, more and more information can be obtained about galaxies more and more distant in the universe. Already some information is being obtained about the universe ten thousand million light years away. But this information does not apply to what the universe may be like out there *now*; the very method of stating the distance means that the radiation has taken ten thousand million or 10^{10} years to reach us. Thus we are already looking back into the past at a sample of the universe as it was 10^{10} years ago—a time that is almost as large as the Hubble time constant itself.

If the universe is really changing according to a "big bang" type of hypothesis, there is no doubt that 10^{10} years ago the matter of the universe should have been closer together, and in particular any galaxies which had formed should have been closer together than we observe them today from earth.

If with these observations it is found that the galaxies 10^{10} light years away are very much closer together, the "Steady State" theory may well have to be abandoned; conversely, it would receive further strength if a sample of the universe 10^{10} years ago looks, on the average, the same as we see around us today.

If the "Steady State" theory is found to hold, there can be no question as to when the universe started nor can there be a question as to how old it is. The universe would simply be infinite in space and time, continually expanding, and with new matter coming into existence to maintain a constant density. On this basis Mach's Principle could still apply but the mass of an object would now remain constant and time would "forever" be "flowing uniformly".

Relativity

It would be remiss of us if we completed these chapters without some mention of the subject of relativity, even though this is to be treated in considerable detail in the lectures by Professor Bondi.

The whole subject of what is called *Special Relativity* was propounded by Einstein on the basis of a famous experimental result. Towards the end of the last century, experiments by two physicists, Michelson and Morley, showed that *the speed of light is a constant of the universe.* No matter what the state of motion of someone who measures the speed of light, this observer always obtains the same value. It is, for example, impossible to "run away" from light as one can do with sound. A space ship, which has taken off from earth, can accelerate for as long as it likes out into space and a light signal from earth will always catch it up; indeed, observers on the space ship would measure the speed of such a light signal to be the same universal constant as anyone else would obtain.

Special relativity discusses a comparison between different observers or different frames of reference, all of which are inertial frames, but in uniform motion relative to each other. One of the main conclusions is that any one of these observers, after communication with a second by means of light signals, must automatically assume that time is running more slowly for the second observer.

Let us give an example by considering an imaginary space ship. Suppose a space ship has taken off from earth, has accelerated to some very high speed, has escaped the earth's gravitational field, and is now drifting through space with its rockets turned off at a uniform speed v away from the earth. This space ship is in an inertial frame as it is moving with uniform velocity relative to the earth through space. Let us suppose that, by a prearranged plan, it has been agreed that the space ship will send us signals at regular intervals—for example, every quarter of an hour or every hour or every 24 hours. For the sake of definiteness let us assume that it is every hour. Then we would normally expect the signals to be reaching us at intervals in excess of one hour because of the added distance each successive signal has to travel. Indeed we would expect the signals to be reaching us every $(1 + v/c)$ hours, where c is the speed of light. But, lo and behold, when we use the fact that c is a uniform constant, it can be shown using simple algebra that the time interval between the signals reaching us must be

$$\frac{1 + v/c}{\sqrt{1 - v^2/c^2}} \text{ hours.}$$

The only way we have of interpreting this is that the space ship's clocks have slowed down so that the space ship is not sending signals every hour at all but at every $\dfrac{1}{\sqrt{1 - v^2/c^2}}$ hours. This is called the relativistic time dilation effect.

Even if the space ship is travelling uniformly towards us at speed v, and we would be expecting signals to be reaching us every $(1 - v/c)$ hours they would still be reaching us at time intervals longer than this by the same time dilation factor.

This leads us, as an interesting sidelight, to the famous *Clock Paradox*. Suppose the space ship of our example takes off from earth and goes on a prolonged space voyage. As long as it is going away from us we must assume that its clocks are running slow compared to ours, and similarly on its return voyage the same is still true. Thus when the space ship returns and lands we would have to expect that it has passed through less time than earth has; the space ship might have been away for five years according to our clocks, but to the space ship's clocks and everybody in the space ship the time of the journey may have been considerably less—say, six months. (We are assuming here that the space ship was actually able to travel quite close to the speed of light.) Is such a thing theoretically possible?

The apparent paradox arises if one imagines oneself on the space ship. To the space traveller the earth is first moving away from him and therefore the time on earth appears to be passing more slowly; then, after he turns around, the earth moves back towards him, with its time again travelling more slowly. Would not the space traveller then find that the earth had passed through less time than he had?

In view of our discussion in this chapter there is a very real difference between the two observers or frames of reference. One, the earth—which is considered to be at least very close to an inertial frame—has remained so during the period of time of the space trip. The other, the space ship, has had to accelerate in order to remove itself from the environment of the earth and solar system, and has had to accelerate again in turning around in space in order to return. Thus it has been removed from an inertial system during these manoeuvres and, according to Mach's Principle, has been subjected to the new gravitational influences from the universe which are occasioned by such accelerations. Irrespective of the details of Mach's Principle, this type of situation is considered in Einstein's Theory of General Relativity, with the conclusion that the overall time passed through on the space ship would indeed be less than on earth. This is the conclusion that one reaches as an earth observer, noting that the space ship's time appears always to be running slow. The space travellers would have been on a journey through *space and time,* and the fact that the space ship would not always be an inertial system, but would undergo strong and prolonged accelerations with respect to the "matter average" of the universe, leads to the prediction that when they finally returned to earth the travellers would have passed through less time than the earth itself.

Thus it is not mere science fiction but an actual prediction of general relativity that, if it were ever to prove technically possible for space travellers to journey at speeds close to that of light to far distant stars, the travellers could well return and find that, what was a ten year trip for them, saw the passage of say a hundred or more years on earth.

This brief glimpse into some of the fascinating aspects of relativity, concluding our actual lectures for the present summer school, has been extracted from our much fuller lectures on this subject at the 1963 summer school. For your interest we are including these lectures in this book as chapters 5 and 6 which follow.

Our remarks on relativity should serve not only to whet your appetites for the lectures of Professor Bondi, but as yet another example of the intricate aspects of the fundamental concept—time. Not only have we seen that the passage of time is fundamentally connected with the universe in general, but we now see that the rate of passage of time can depend on our state of motion in the universe.

CHAPTER 5

Velocity of Light and the Theory of Relativity

(a) Velocity of Light

The velocity of light through vacuum—usually designated by the symbol c—is one of the most fundamental quantities in science. To be more precise, c is the velocity of propagation of the electric field; the fact that this is finite then gives rise to what we have called magnetic phenomena. It is also clear that with c being the basic velocity of propagation of the electric field, precisely this same velocity must automatically be the velocity with which all electro-magnetic radiation travels. It does not matter whether we are talking about electro-magnetic radiation of radio frequencies, light frequencies or X-ray frequencies, it must always travel with this basic velocity c.

A. Michelson   *A. Einstein*

As to be expected the first measurement of this velocity was actually obtained by observing light, and hence the name " velocity of light " has been retained for c despite the fact that it must automatically also be the velocity of all other types of electro-magnetic radiation.

It is interesting that the first even approximate measurement of the velocity of light involved the planet Jupiter and its moons. Jupiter is orbiting the sun a distance 5·2 times further out than the earth. It is a very large planet with a mass some 318 times that of the Earth. One of the most interesting things about Jupiter is its system of 12 known moons. The four brightest were seen by Galileo, the inventor of the telescope, in 1610 and since then eight other smaller moons of Jupiter have been observed. The four bright satellites of Jupiter are comparable in size to our own moon, and the two largest are actually bigger than the planet Mercury. But for their close proximity to Jupiter we would be able to see at least three of them easily with the naked eye, and they can readily be discerned with field glasses.

The periods of revolution of these four moons range from 1 day 18 hours for the one closest to Jupiter, up to 16 days 16 hours for the one furthest out. Their orbits are quite close to the plane of the ecliptic and therefore each of these moons disappears from our view behind Jupiter for a time once in each complete revolution. This is called an eclipse of the moon in question. It was in 1675 that Ole Roemer reported observations on the eclipses of Jupiter's moons which allowed him to estimate the velocity of light through vacuum.

He consistently observed the eclipses of one of Jupiter's four bright moons over the period of a year starting from a time when the Earth and Jupiter were as close to each other as possible. He obtained the at first surprising result that the time taken for a certain number of eclipses to occur during the first six months was slightly longer than for the same number of eclipses during the second six months. This he interpreted as being due to a finite velocity of propagation of the light coming from the particular moon under observation*. The moon itself, of course, must always keep moving with a constant period of revolution ; thus the effect must only be an apparent one and not due to any real fluctuations in period of the moon itself. Roemer's argument can be followed through in the following manner :

If the Earth and Jupiter are at their closest approach to each other at a certain time, then close to six months later they will be separated by the greatest possible distance, since the period of Jupiter (11·9 years) is much greater than that of the Earth. The difference between the two distances is essentially equal to the diameter of the Earth's

---

* We observe all planets and moons in the solar system by means of light from the sun being reflected from them to us.

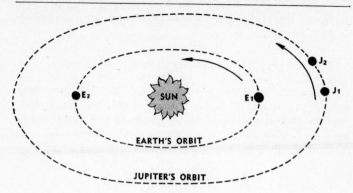

Figure 5·1

This diagram (not to scale) illustrates how the velocity of light was measured by Roemer.

orbit around the sun—see Figure 5.1. Suppose the interval between eclipses by Jupiter of the moon in question is t. Then, while the Earth is moving away from Jupiter (during the first six months), eclipses apparently occur later and later than they would if the Earth and Jupiter had remained in the same position; this is due to the extra time taken by the light to cross the increasing gap between the two planets.

Let T_1 be the time taken for N eclipses occurring in the interval (six months) between E_1J_1 and E_2J_2 (Figure 5·1). Since we must allow for the time taken to cross E_1E_2 this is

$$T_1 = Nt - \frac{D}{c} . \qquad . \qquad . \qquad . \quad (5\cdot1)$$

where D is the diameter of the earth's orbit and c is the velocity of light in vacuum. Similarly, during the second half of the year, N eclipses take a different time T_2 given by

$$T_2 = Nt + \frac{D}{c}, \qquad . \qquad . \qquad . \quad (5\cdot2)$$

By subtracting equation (5·2) from (5·1) we find the difference in time $T_1 - T_2$ for the N eclipses during the first six months compared to N eclipses during the second six months.

$$T_1 - T_2 = 2\frac{D}{c}. \qquad . \qquad . \qquad . \quad (5\cdot3)$$

Roemer himself observed this time difference to be $16 \cdot 5$ minutes so that he obtained

$$\frac{D}{c} = 16 \cdot 5 \text{ minutes.}$$

The value of c obtained by Roemer from this result was rather approximate because he did not have an accurate knowledge of the diameter of the orbit of the Earth. If we insert the at present known value for D of approximately 300 million kilometres (3×10^{13} cm) we immediately have

$$c = \frac{3 \times 10^{13}}{16 \cdot 5 \times 60} \text{ cm/sec.}$$

$$= \frac{3 \times 10^{13}}{990}$$

$$\simeq 3 \times 10^{10} \text{ cm/sec.}$$

Roemer's method is thus capable of giving at least an approximate estimate of the velocity of light, and incidentally we notice that since light takes $16\frac{1}{4}$ minutes to cross the diameter of the Earth's orbit, the light from the sun itself must be taking $8\frac{1}{4}$ minutes to reach us.

In the years following this first observation more and more accurate methods of measuring the velocity of light have been devised. Foucault devised a reasonably accurate laboratory method in 1850. He obtained the value $c = 2 \cdot 98 \times 10^{10}$ cm/sec. Between 1926 and 1933 a very accurate series of laboratory measurements was performed by Michelson and collaborators, who obtained the result $c = (2 \cdot 99796 \pm 0 \cdot 00004) \times 10^{10}$ cm/sec for the velocity of light in vacuum.

By now a whole series of extremely accurate measurements have been performed not only on light but also on other wave-lengths of electro-magnetic radiation, and the accepted value at present is

$$c = (2 \cdot 997924 \pm 0 \cdot 00001) \times 10^{10} \text{ cm/sec.}$$

Every accurate observation has confirmed that this velocity of propagation of electrical influences through vacuum is a fundamental constant of nature, and all electro-magnetic radiation is a propagated through vacuum with this speed.

(b) The Michelson-Morley Experiment

We have by now gained some insight into why the velocity of light c is one of the fundamental constants of nature, and we have seen how measurements of this quantity date as far back as 1675. At present it is known to extremely high accuracy.

At this stage however, we should ask ourselves the question which scientists were asking towards the end of the last century. This question is *"to what is this velocity of light referred?"* The situation can be more clearly stated in analogy to the case of sound. As we know, sound propagates with a certain velocity v_s through the atmosphere of the Earth. This velocity is a property of the atmosphere itself and is related to the normal kinetic motion of the atoms and molecules within the atmosphere. Thus the velocity of sound in air is v_s *relative to the air.*

If a train which is stationary blows its whistle, the sound propagates through the air at the velocity v_s relative to the air. A stationary listener some distance d away hears the sound at time $t = \dfrac{d}{v_s}$ after the whistle was blown (assuming a still atmosphere).

If instead the train had been moving at the time it blew its whistle a stationary listener at some distance d away would still hear the sound at a time $t = \dfrac{d}{r_s}$ later, because the sound propagates through the atmosphere with velocity v_s quite independent of how the source was moving at the time. As we know the apparent frequency heard by the listener changes (Doppler Effect), but the velocity of propagation of the sound through the atmosphere is a constant.

However if the listener himself is moving, the time interval will be different. For example, if a listener moves towards a source of sound at velocity v the sound will, of course, then approach him with the velocity $v_s + v$. The listener is, in fact, " running into the sound " and will, therefore, hear it sooner than he would have had he remained stationary. Similarly, if the listener moves away from the source of sound with speed v, the sound only catches up on him at the *relative speed* $v_s - v$.

Thus with sound the constant speed involved is the *speed of sound* v_s *with respect to the atmosphere.* Any observer at rest with respect to the atmosphere will naturally observe that the speed of sound is

v_s. But if an observer is moving at speed v with respect to the atmosphere he will observe a speed of sound equal to $v + v_s$ for sounds that are emitted in front of him, or $v_s - v$ for sounds that are emitted behind him ; in general, therefore, the speed of sound which he actually observes *relative to himself* depends on his own motion through the atmosphere.

What is the case for light? After all, we, as observers on the Earth, are moving if for no other reason than that the Earth itself is moving in its orbit around the sun at about 30 km/sec (3×10^6 cm/sec). Thus if we look at a particular distant star at a certain time of the year, we might be moving *towards* the star at 3×10^6 cm/sec. If we observe the star again 6 months later, we will then be moving *away* from it at 3×10^6 cm/sec. We might, therefore, expect to obtain slightly different values for the velocity of light coming from the star *relative* to us.

But first we must ask: what is the "thing" with respect to which the velocity of light is a constant? After all, in the case of sound, it is the atmosphere—the velocity through the atmosphere is v_s. But in the case of light from distant stars, the light is travelling through a vacuum, and to say that the velocity of light is a constant *with respect to* a vacuum is meaningless.

It was because of this that by the end of the last century an idea had become established that the entire universe must be filled with some "stuff" which is "at rest" in the universe and which we call the vacuum. This all pervading stuff throughout the universe was called the ether. It was assumed that the ether had no physical properties by which we could detect it and that it would appear to us precisely as vacuum. However, material objects were assumed to be able to move without friction through the ether. Thus the ether was considered to be at rest and all the planets, suns and galaxies of the universe were moving through the "stationary" ether.

The only property that the ether was assumed to have was that electro-magnetic radiation would propagate through it with a speed relative to the ether which was a constant of the universe, say c. Thus the ether was invoked purely to take the place for light that the atmosphere is for sound.

For any source of light moving with respect to the ether the light was still considered to propagate through the ether at this universal constant speed c. But if an observer were moving towards the source with a speed relative to the ether of v, then he would observe the speed of light from that source to be $c + v$. Similarly, if he were moving away from the source he would observe the speed of light relative to himself to be $c - v$.

It is now known that this is, in fact, wrong and that the whole idea of the ether was a myth. However, to prove it wrong required some very detailed experiments, the results of which led Einstein to his famous theory of relativity. In order to achieve some idea of the basis of this theory we must follow through the arguments which first led to the ether postulate and to the type of experiment which disproved it.

At the moment it possibly seems quite logical to you that somehow an observer should get different values for the velocity of light depending on how he himself is moving. Let us, therefore, for the moment accept the ether idea and see where it leads us.

If there were such a thing as an ether "at rest" in the universe the Earth would certainly be moving through it. Even if at a certain instant the Earth happened to have zero speed relative to the ether this would only be momentarily, because the Earth is following its almost circular orbit around the Sun at its speed of about 3×10^6 cm/sec. Then again, the Sun itself has a velocity of about $1 \cdot 9 \times 10^6$ cm/sec relative to the nearest stars. In addition our whole galaxy is moving with a speed well in excess of 10^7 cm/sec relative to other "near" galaxies in the universe. Thus there is no doubt that we would be moving through the ether with a speed at least 3×10^6 cm/sec on the average, and the direction of our velocity would vary through the year as we proceed in our circular orbit.

Light produced even from a source on Earth would then move with its velocity c relative to the ether, since this would be (as in the case of sound) independent of any motion of the source. If we measure the velocity of this light relative to us, however, the value we get should depend on our own velocity relative to the ether. If our speed relative to the ether is v we should get the value $c - v$ for light shining along our direction of motion, and the value $c + v$ for light moving opposite to our direction of motion. Of course, if the value of v is only 3×10^6 cm/sec compared with a value of c of 3×10^{10} cm/sec, we would be looking for an extremely small effect.

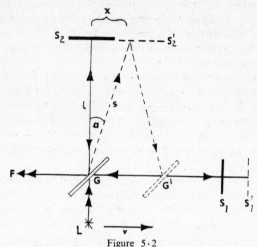

Figure 5·2
Diagram of Michelson - Morley experiment.

It was, however, pointed out by Maxwell in 1878 that this effect should be detectable. Such an experiment was first performed in 1880-81 by A. A. Michelson in the Physics Institute of Berlin University, and was repeated with very great care by Michelson and Morley in Cleveland in 1887. This experiment was destined to become very famous and is termed the Michelson-Morley experiment.

The principle of the experiment is illustrated diagrammatically in Figure 5·2. A beam of light from a source L impinges on a glass plate inclined at 45 degrees to the beam of light. The plate is so chosen that some of the light is reflected at right angles to the initial beam and the other half is transmitted through undeviated. Each beam travels an equal distance l to a mirror, is reflected and comes back on its track to the glass plate. Now, half the light reflected from mirror S_1 (see diagram) will be transmitted through the glass plate G and similarly half the light reflected from the mirror S_2 will be reflected by the glass plate. These two beams are then merged into one and can be detected and studied in detail by optical instruments designated schematically by F in the diagram.

Each of the two beams which merge at F has travelled along its own particular path and one has been reflected by the mirror

S_1 and the other by the mirror S_2. Although the two paths GS_1 and GS_2 are adjusted quite accurately to the same length l, it is clear that these lengths will not be accurately equal compared to the wave-length of light — there is always bound to be a slight difference in length which certainly exceeds the wave-length involved in the light being used. Thus when they are brought together at F the two beams will be somewhat "out of phase" with each other. This is just the same as in sound when "interference effects" can be observed between two beams of sound which may have originated from the same source but have travelled different courses. In the present case when the electric magnetic intensities are a maximum for beam 1 at some point at F, they will not be a maximum for beam 2, and vice versa. The optical apparatus at F can produce what is called an interference pattern when the two beams are combined, the nature of which is dependent on the difference in length of the paths that they have followed.

Quite apart from actual physical differences in the path-lengths GS_1 and GS_2, another effect would come into play if, in fact, there were an ether, for the whole apparatus located on the earth would be moving through the ether. Suppose, for example, that it is moving with velocity v through the ether in the direction of the path GS_1. Since the velocity of light on the ether assumption is always a constant c relative to the ether, the velocity with respect to our apparatus would vary. The light would travel out along GS_1 with a relative velocity $c - v$ and back along the path S_1G with a relative velocity $c + v$. The total time t_1 for the light to travel from G to S_1 and back to G would thus be

$$t_1 = \frac{l}{c - v} + \frac{l}{c + v},$$

$$= \frac{2l}{c} \; \frac{1}{1 - \frac{v^2}{c^2}}. \qquad \cdot \quad \cdot \quad \cdot \quad \cdot \quad (5 \cdot 4)$$

This is slightly different from the value $\frac{2l}{c}$ which we would have if v were zero.

Similarly, with the apparatus moving through the ether the other mirror S_2 will be also moving. In the time taken for the light to travel from G to S_2 the mirror would have moved sideways by a small amount, and the reflection would take place at the point shown. By the time the light has returned, the glass plate has moved on to a new position, G'—see figure $5 \cdot 2$. Thus, in reality, the path travelled by this beam is along the two sides of the isosceles triangle shown. Let the length of the base GG' be denoted by $2 x$, and the length of one of the sides be s. Then we have

$$s^2 = l^2 + x^2. \qquad . \qquad . \qquad . \qquad (5 \cdot 5)$$

But in turn the glass plate has moved a distance x at its velocity v when the light has moved a distance s at velocity c. Thus the ratio x must be equal to $\dfrac{v}{c}$. On substituting $x = \dfrac{v}{c} s$ in equation $(5 \cdot 5)$ we have

$$s^2 = l^2 + s^2 \left(\frac{v^2}{c^2} \right). \qquad . \qquad . \qquad . \qquad (5 \cdot 6)$$

Thus

$$s = \frac{l}{\sqrt{1 - \dfrac{v^2}{c^2}}}. \qquad . \qquad . \qquad (5 \cdot 7)$$

The time taken for beam 2 to travel up and back the distance $2 s$ is thus

$$t_2 = \frac{2l}{c} \frac{1}{\sqrt{1 - \dfrac{v^2}{c^2}}}. \qquad . \qquad . \qquad . \qquad . \qquad (5 \cdot 8)$$

Thus quite apart from any actual physical difference in the path-lengths the times taken for the light to travel the two paths will differ by the amount

$$t_1 - t_2 = \frac{2l}{c} \left\{ \frac{1}{1 - \dfrac{v^2}{c^2}} - \frac{1}{\sqrt{1 - \dfrac{v^2}{c^2}}} \right\},$$

$$= \frac{2l}{c} \frac{1}{\sqrt{1 - \dfrac{v^2}{c^2}}} \left\{ \frac{1}{\sqrt{1 - \dfrac{v^2}{c^2}}} - 1 \right\}. \qquad . \qquad . \qquad (5 \cdot 9)$$

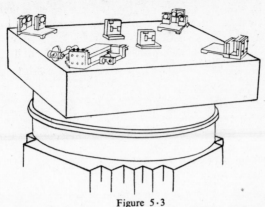

Figure 5·3
The apparatus used in the Michelson - Morley experiment.

This difference tends to zero of course, when the velocity v is zero, but for a finite velocity it contributes an additional effective path difference for the two beams. In this case, the interference pattern observed will depend on this additional effective path difference.

Now a crucial part of the Michelson-Morley experiment was that the whole optical apparatus was mounted on a block of sandstone floating in mercury, so that the whole system could be rotated without serious vibrations during the course of observations (Figure 5·3). Rotation through 45 degrees from the position represented in Figure 5·2 would bring both arms GS_1 and GS_2 into the same inclination to the direction of motion, so that by symmetry the velocity effects are the same for both and the time difference (equation 5·9) will disappear. A further rotation through another 45 degrees would just interchange the effect between the two beams, and so on.

As the apparatus is rotated, therefore it is clear that a change in the interference effects between the two light beams should be observed, as long as the Earth is moving with some speed v with respect to the ether. And even if the experiment happened to indicate zero velocity at one time of the year, it should certainly indicate a finite velocity v, say 6 months later. Indeed the minimum possible speed v which could really be anticipated is the orbital speed of the earth of 3×10^6 cm/sec.

The far-reaching result of the Michelson-Morley experiment was that the *interference effects between the two light beams remained absolutely constant, independent of the amount of rotation of the apparatus or the time of year.* The accuracy of the experiment could not rule out the possibility of velocities less than about $\frac{1}{2} \times 10^6$ cm/sec, but this was certainly enough to show that there was no effect whatsoever of the earth's orbital velocity of 3×10^6 cm/-sec (which should have been the absolute minimum speed of the earth with respect to the ether).

Towards the end of the last century many other experiments of a similar kind were performed. All such experiments yielded the same negative result that *absolutely no motion of the earth relative to the ether could be detected.*

(c) Einstein's Theory of Relativity

This result of the Michelson-Morley and similar experiments caused consternation among the scientists. In the case of sound the equivalent experiment to a Michelson-Morley experiment certainly yielded positive results. The sound travels with speed v_s in the atmosphere, and an observer moving with speed v with respect to the atmosphere could if needs be, determine his speed by "Michelson-Morley type" experiments on sound. But in the case of light it seemed that no matter how the observer was moving, it was impossible for any experiment to detect this motion. In the case of the Michelson-Morley experiment — Figure 5·2 — the result showed that despite the velocity of the apparatus v the light travelling from G to the mirror S_1 had a constant velocity c relative to the apparatus, and similarly that the light travelling to mirror S_2 had a constant speed c with respect to the apparatus, completely independent of v.

This result produced many far-fetched theories in attempted explanation. One such theory was "the earth carried its ether along with it". This theory envisaged an ether as not being totally at rest within the universe, but that each material body was surrounded by ether which it carried along with it. All such attempted explanations were, however, unconvincing and gave no real physical understanding of the phenomenon.

It was in 1905 that Einstein developed his Theory of Relativity based on the results of the Michelson-Morley experiment. He took the attitude, which had now become accepted in modern physics, that it is absurd to try to invoke an ether and to give it peculiar properties purely because we think that light should behave in a manner analogous to sound in the atmosphere. After all, an ether was something which we could never detect and was purely a fictitious substance introduced to enable us to think of light moving throughout the universe in the same way as we think of sound moving through the atmosphere.

Einstein's philosophy was as follows:—

Let us be satisfied with our understanding of the Maxwell electro-magnetic equations and the fact that electro-magnetic radiation will propagate through vacuum. Secondly, let us take as a fundamental experimental fact that the *velocity of light as measured in a vacuum is always the constant c no matter what the state of motion of the observer**.

Thus just as Newton's Law of Gravitation, for example, is an experimentally established law, so it is to be considered an experimentally established law that the velocity of light *relative* to any observer is the constant c *no matter how the observer is moving*. Just as the law of gravitation is accepted and can be used as the basis for an understanding of the motion of bodies and the gravitational forces, so we must accept this law regarding the velocity of light. We can then ask: what logical consequences can be predicted on the basis of this law?

As Einstein pointed out, an immediate consequence is the preservation of the so-called *relativity principle of mechanics,* which holds for uniform motion in a straight line. Consider a ball which is thrown upwards by a person travelling in a railway carriage with uniform speed along a straight track. As observed by the person in the carriage, the motion of the ball is just the same as if the carriage were at rest; when the ball is thrown vertically upwards it reaches its maximum height and falls vertically downwards again. Although the path of the ball is a straight line as viewed by the person in the carriage, if seen by a person standing beside the railway line it would be a curved parabola. This observer could, in principle,

---

* The velocity of light in air differs very little from the velocity in vacuum.

photograph the parabola and hence determine the velocity of the train relative to the ground. On the other hand, the observer who is travelling in the train cannot possibly deduce anything about his own uniform straight line motion from the behaviour of the ball. Of course, whenever the train is accelerated, e.g., by going around a curve, the ball no longer falls vertically downwards. Accelerated motion can thus be detected from within the moving system, but the relativity principle of mechanics holds for uniform motion in a straight line and says that "the uniform straight line motion of a system cannot be detected by means of any mechanical process taking place within the system".

The same would be true, for example, in a space-ship. If the space-ship does not have its rocket motors turned on and is just drifting with uniform speed through space, there is absolutely no way that any experiment performed inside the ship can tell what the speed is. Indeed this is quite reasonable because after all, what is the speed? It will have one value relative to the earth, another relative to the sun, another relative to a distant star, and so on, but as far as the people in the ship are concerned, all this is irrelevant —to them, they might as well be at rest.

However, if the ether theory had been correct, this would not be completely true. The occupants of the space-ship could have performed a Michelson-Morley experiment and determined how fast they were going with respect to the "stationary" and all pervading ether. Thus experiments on electro-magnetic radiation within a system would have been able to determine the "absolute velocity" of that system through space. The negative result of the Michelson-Morley experiment showed that this is not the case and that even experiments using electro-magnetic radiation cannot detect any absolute motion. Thus it becomes completely general that all the laws of physics within a uniformly moving space-ship are exactly the same as in any other uniformly moving system, and it is meaningless to ask which system is at rest in the universe. Anything is moving only with respect to something else, and there is no absolute standard to say which one, if either, might happen to be "stationary".

In the words of Einstein there is no "preferred system" in the universe; the laws of physics in any one system are exactly the same

as in any other system moving with uniform straight line motion
with respect to the first. Indeed, so logical did this seem to Einstein,
and so logical does it seem to scientists of today, that very often the
principle of equivalence of observers in uniform relative motion is
stated as a *logical premise* for the theory of relativity — without
requiring a discussion of its experimental verification by the
Michelson-Morley experiment. This is the attitude taken by
Professor Bondi in his lectures on relativity.

This principle of equivalence of observers may sound very
obvious and it may seem, at first, as if the law regarding the constancy of the speed of light, as determined by any observer irrespective of his own motion, is interesting but of no great consequence.
Nothing could be further from the truth. Consider, for example, the
following situation. A space-ship has taken off from Earth, has
accelerated to some very high speed, has escaped the Earth's
gravitational field, and is now drifting through space with its
rockets turned off at a speed away from the Earth which, for
argument's sake, we might imagine to be half the speed of light

$$\left(\text{ i.e., } \frac{c}{2} \right).$$

Suppose now we wish to make contact with the occupants of this
space-ship. The only way in which we can do so is by means of
electro-magnetic radiation. We can, for example, send a radio signal
out to the space-ship.

Such a radio signal leaves us at the velocity of light c. We might,
at first, imagine therefore that it would only overhaul the space-ship
with a speed $\frac{c}{2}$, but this is contrary to the basic law on the velocity
of light. The velocity of light must always be the same relative to
any observer irrespective of his own state of motion. *Thus the
radio signal must still overhaul the space-ship with a velocity c relative to the space-ship.* In other words, if an occupant of the space-
ship were to measure how rapidly this radio signal went past him
he must obtain the same value c.

This seems impossible. How can a radio signal leave the earth
with a velocity c and yet still be measured to be travelling with a
velocity c by occupants of the space-ship which is itself moving with
a velocity $\frac{c}{2}$ away from the earth. *Einstein pointed out that the*

only way out of this dilemma is for an observer on earth to assume that the rate of progress of time has slowed down on the space-ship due to its motion away from the earth. This is our only way out if we are to find the situation understandable. If a radio signal leaves us with velocity c and travels towards a space-ship also moving away with velocity $\frac{c}{2}$ we can only assume that it is catching up on a space-ship with a speed less than c. When we know from the basic law, however, that observers on the space-ship must measure the velocity of the signal relative to the ship also to be c, we must assume that time for them is passing more slowly than for us. For, of course, the velocity c which they measure is in so many cm/sec in terms of *their* seconds, and if their seconds are appropriately longer than ours, they can still obtain the value c for a velocity which we think should be less than c.

Of course, everything is purely relative. If the occupants of the space-ship send a return radio signal to us they know the signal leaves them with the velocity c. At the same time, to them the earth is moving away with velocity $\frac{c}{2}$. Thus they would expect their signal to overhaul the earth only with the speed $\frac{c}{2}$. The fact that they know, from the basic law of light, that the inhabitants of the earth still measure this signal to be reaching them with the velocity c can only be understood by them if they assume that the progress of time on earth is slower than on the space-ship.

In the above example we assumed the space-ship to be moving away from the earth with the velocity $\frac{c}{2}$, but, of course, the argument is the same for any such speed v. Let us assume that the space-ship is moving relative to the earth with speed v. Then it was shown by Einstein that to us the progress of time on the space-ship is apparently so slowed down that one second, for example, of "space-ship time" lasts $\dfrac{1}{\sqrt{1 - \dfrac{v^2}{c^2}}}$ seconds of our time. In general, a time interval t_s seconds of space-ship time would appear to us to be equivalent to a time interval

$$t = \frac{t_s}{\sqrt{1 - \dfrac{v^2}{c^2}}}. \qquad . \qquad . \qquad . \quad (5\cdot10)$$

seconds of our time.

Similarly, however, just the reverse is true for the occupants of the space-ship. They would consider that a time interval t_E earth seconds would, because of the " longer " seconds on earth, be equivalent to a time interval

$$t' = \frac{t_E}{\sqrt{1 - \dfrac{v^2}{c^2}}}, \qquad . \qquad . \quad (5\cdot11)$$

in space-ship seconds.

This apparent slower rate of time, which we attribute to any system moving relative to us, is called the *time dilation effect*. It is often stated to be a prediction of Einstein's Theory of Relativity. This is, of course, true. It is not, however, a consequence of a long complicated theoretical argument, but follows immediately from the experimental fact that we must assume the velocity of light always to be c no matter who measures it or how he is moving. In the years that have passed since Einstein's theory there have been several experiments which indicate that the time dilation effect really occurs.

One such experiment involves a type of particle called a meson which is now known to be a constituent of protons and neutrons. The meson is a particle which only "lives" a short time before breaking up into smaller constituents. Its lifetime has been measured by many and varied experiments which all produce the same result. A meson at rest lives for just $2\cdot6 \times 10^{-8}$ sec.

However, in laboratory experiments it is found that its apparent lifetime increases the faster it is moving, and as the meson attains speed close to the speed of light its apparent lifetime can become very long indeed. This is simply another piece of experimental evidence in agreement with the time dilation effect of Einstein's relativity. It can be understood if we say that, for the moving meson, time is passing slower than for us. Thus a certain number τ seconds for the meson would, in fact, be equivalent to a time interval

$$t = \frac{\tau}{\sqrt{1 - \frac{v^2}{c^2}}}$$ seconds of our time. where v is the velocity of the

meson with respect to us.

When $v = 0,$ $t = \tau$. where $\tau = 2 \cdot 6 \times 10^{-8}$ sec, which is the life-time of the meson in its own system. When it is moving, however,

its apparent lifetime to us increases by just the factor $\dfrac{1}{\sqrt{1 - \dfrac{v^2}{c^2}}}$.

But let us investigate this a little further. We can consider the case of some object which is continuously being accelerated by some accelerating force. In the laboratory it is, for example, possible to subject electrons and other fundamental charged particles to a continuous accelerating force. When such a particle is continually being subjected to a strong accelerating force its acceleration should be constant according to the equation $F = ma$, where F is the accelerating force, m the mass of the particle, and a the acceleration. Thus the velocity of our particle should continuously be increasing, eventually passing the velocity of light, and still increasing.

Yet we have just seen that as far as we are concerned no particle— or anything for that matter—can travel faster than, or even equal to, the velocity of light.

This apparently poses a paradox. How is it possible for a particle to be subjected continuously to an accelerating force, yet never be accelerated faster than the velocity of light, no matter for how long a force acts? Once again, Einstein pointed out that the only way we can make sense of this situation is for us to say that as far as we are concerned *the mass of the particle must increase with its speed* in such a way as to make the acceleration less and less the higher the speed.

Let us call the mass of the particle when it is at rest in the laboratory m_o; this "rest mass" is the mass that we have normally been talking about for all objects. In fact, Einstein showed that when the particle is moving with respect to us the only way we can make

sense of what we observe is to attribute to the moving particle a
mass m which is given by

$$m = \frac{m_o}{\sqrt{1 - \dfrac{v^2}{c^2}}}, \qquad . \quad . \quad . \quad (5 \cdot 12)$$

where v is the instantaneous velocity of the particle. It should be
noted that the mass m tends to become infinitely large as the speed
v approaches the speed of light. Thus no force can ever accelerate
the object even up to the speed of light because it would become
infinitely massive. In fact, if a force F acts on a particle (for argument's sake always in the same direction), the acceleration a along
this direction can be shown to be given by the equation.*

$$F = \frac{m_o a}{(1 - v^2/c^2)^{3/2}} \qquad . \quad . \quad . \quad (5 \cdot 13)$$

Thus $\qquad a = \frac{F}{m_o} (1 - v^2/c^2)^{3/2}. \qquad . \quad . \quad . \quad (5 \cdot 14)$

From this equation it is obvious that for very low speeds $\left(\dfrac{v}{c} << 1 \right)$
the factor $(1 - v^2/c^2)^{3/2}$ is negligibly different from unity and we
have the ordinary Newtonian result. However, as v increases towards
the velocity of light the factor $(1 - v^2/c^2)^{3/2}$ becomes smaller and
smaller ; the acceleration becomes less and less, and thus the force
becomes less and less effective in producing acceleration. In the
limit, $v = c$, the acceleration is identically zero and hence no force
can produce a speed v which is greater than c.

---

* Recall that the definition of force is given by:
  Force = time rate of change of momentum mv.
  In the Newtonian case the mass m is assumed not to vary ($m = m_o$) and hence—
  Force $= (m) \times$ (time rate of change of velocity v),
  $\qquad = (m) \times$ (acceleration a),
  $\qquad = ma = m_o a$.
  However, since we now have that the mass m does vary according to equation
  (5.12), we no longer can simply remove it from the bracket and the expression
  for the force becomes :
  Force = time rate of change of momentum mv,
  $\qquad = (m) \times$ (time rate of change of velocity v) $+ (v) \times$ (time rate
  $\qquad\qquad$ of change of mass m),
  $\qquad = ma + (m_o v) \times$ [time rate of change of $(1 - v^2/c^2)^{-\frac{1}{2}}$].
  This expression simplifies to that given by equation (5.13).

This experiment has been performed extremely accurately with results in excellent agreement with the Einstein time dilation formula.

In the above we have seen qualitatively how the law of light and the principle of equivalence leads logically to the so-called time dilation effects. The actual formulae, such as equation (5.10) or (5.11), have simply been stated without derivation. We shall now show. however, how such formulae can be quite simply derived.

(d) Time Dilation and Doppler Effect

We will now consider the same type of examples as in the previous section, but this time with a view to actually deriving the formulae. Let us imagine two people, A and B, who are capable of making observations, and who are moving away from each other with uniform speed. In the language of relativity these are called *observers*, and as far as A is concerned, B is moving away from him at constant speed. As we saw in the last section A must assume that B's time is running slower than his own and let us now see how A would calculate this effect in detail.

Suppose A sends regular light or radio signals to B once every t seconds—he must assume that they arrive at B with a different interval of time between signals, say τ, according to B's clock. In order to calculate what this time τ is, A can write $\tau = kt$ and can proceed to deduce what k must be by two successive arguments.*

(1) Suppose there is another observer A_1 who is **at rest** relative to A but well separated from him. Indeed let us imagine that A_1 is directly in B's path so that B is travelling towards A_1. Now if A_1 picks up A's regular signals he will clearly be receiving them at intervals of t seconds—i.e., at the same intervals as A is emitting them —since A_1 is not moving relative to A. But since the velocity of light relative to A and A_1 is always c it is irrelevant whether or not the signals are interrupted by B and instantaneously transmitted again—they must still arrive at A_1 at intervals of t seconds.

Thus A is faced with the following conclusion : if he sends signals every t seconds, B receives them every $\tau = kt$ seconds ; and if B transmits signals every $\tau = kt$ seconds, A_1 receives them every t seconds. Thus when B emits signals at regular intervals τ they arrive at A_1 at regular intervals τ/k. This gives us our first

---

*The first step in our determination of k is the same as that given in the lectures by Professor Bondi, and introduced by him in his very successful lectures for the 1962 Summer School.

important result ; if k is the multiplying factor relating to two observers moving **apart** with uniform speed v, then $1/k$ is the corresponding multiplying factor when they are moving **together** with speed v. In other words a time interval t for A will correspond to a time interval $\tau = kt$ for B when B is moving away from A at *speed* v, but it will correspond to a time interval $\tau = t/k$ if B were moving towards A with uniform speed v.

This is one piece of information concerning the value of k which is extremely useful for its determination.

(2) Now let us imagine a different condition, although one in which B is still moving relative to A at uniform speed v. Suppose that B is first moving towards A, passes A's position, and then moves away from A. Now we can imagine that A has made preparation in advance, knowing that B is going to come along, in order to make some measurements. Suppose that at regular points along B's track, at a distance, say, x apart, A has arranged little signal boxes each of which will be stimulated to send out a flash of light when B passes it. A then sits next to one of these signal boxes and waits for B to come along.

Eventually B, who is moving at uniform speed v towards A, passes the first signal box and the first flash of light is sent. Thereafter A receives light flashes at regular intervals as B passes successive signal boxes. The time interval between these flashes received by A may be readily calculated. Suppose one signal box is a distance X away from A. The light signal, having been fired by B's passing, takes a time X/c to reach A. B then takes x/v seconds to reach the next signal box and its signal takes a time $\dfrac{X - x}{c}$ to reach A. The time interval t_1 between the signals reaching A is the difference between $\dfrac{x}{v} + \dfrac{X - x}{c}$ and $\dfrac{X}{c}$. Thus as far as A is concerned the time interval, say t_1, between successive signals reaching him is

$$t_1 = \frac{x}{v} + \frac{X - x}{c} - \frac{X}{c}$$

$$= \frac{x}{cv} (c - v) \quad .. \quad .. \quad .. \quad .. \quad (5.12)$$

After some time B flashes by A's position, and thereafter is moving away from A with speed v. B is, however, still passing the regularly spaced signal boxes and the successive flashes of light

which they emit are arriving back at A at regular intervals, although
the time between them t_2 is now greater than before. Suppose B
passes one box at distance Y from A. The signal will take a time
Y/c to get back to A. Then B takes a further time x/v to get to the
next signal box and its signal takes a time $\dfrac{Y + x}{c}$ to return to A.
Thus as far as A is concerned the time interval t_2 between the signals
is

$$t_2 = \frac{x}{v} + \frac{Y + x}{c} - \frac{y}{c}$$

$$= \frac{x}{cv} (c + v) \quad .. \quad .. \quad .. \quad .. \quad (5.13)$$

Now as B passes each of these signal boxes in turn he will
see the light flash that each emits instantaneously ; so that as far
as B is concerned he will be passing signal boxes at regular time
intervals, say τ, according to B's clock. Naturally τ will be the
same for B whether he is moving towards A or away from A, for
after all B need not know that A exists. The question is : what is
this time interval τ for B?

We now have the situation where we can introduce our factor
k from argument (1). We know that when B is travelling **towards**
A at speed v, light signals emanating from B at time intervals τ
according to his clock would reach A at time intervals $t_1 = \tau/k$
according to A's clock. Thus from equation (5.12) we have
immediately that

$$\frac{\tau}{k} = \frac{x}{cv} (c - v) \quad .. \quad .. \quad .. \quad .. \quad (5.14)$$

We also know that when B is moving away from A light
emanating from B at regular intervals τ according to his clock,
arrives back at A at intervals $t_2 = k\tau$ according to A's clock.
Hence from equation (5.13) we immediately have that

$$k\tau = \frac{x}{cv} (c + v) \quad .. \quad .. \quad .. \quad .. \quad (5.15)$$

If we now divide equation (5.15) by equation (5.14) we have
the result

$$k^2 = \frac{c + v}{c - v}$$
$$\text{or}$$
$$k = \sqrt{\frac{c + v}{c - v}} \quad .. \quad .. \quad .. \quad (5.16)$$

Another way of writing this value of k is

$$k = \frac{c + v}{\sqrt{c^2 - v^2}} = \frac{1 + \dfrac{v}{c}}{\sqrt{1 - \dfrac{v^2}{c^2}}} \qquad \text{.. (5.17)}$$

It should be recalled that we originally defined k to be the factor which transformed one time into another for two observers moving apart at uniform speed v. For two observers moving together we simply change v to $-v$ for the appropriate formula in this case. We see from equation (5.16) that k then becomes $1/k$.*

When the two observers are moving apart with uniform speed v the factor k in equation (5.17) is greater than unity so that light signals sent at intervals t apart from one will arrive at the other separated by longer time intervals. Of course, part of this increase is to be expected, simply because each signal has to travel more distance than its predecessors. Suppose we have B moving away from A with A sending signals at a time interval t. If the rate of progress of time on B were exactly the same as on A the measured time interval between successive signals arriving at B would be, say, $\tau_0 = k_0 t$ with

$$k_0 = 1 + \frac{v}{c} \qquad \text{.. .. .. .. (5.18)}$$

This is the normal classical effect to be expected simply because each successive signal has further to go. However, the true formula (5.17) is different from this by the factor $\dfrac{1}{\sqrt{1 - \dfrac{v^2}{c^2}}}$ which is the

---

*It is well known that different results are obtained for sound than we have just derived for light. In the case of sound we must remember that the speed of sound is constant only with respect to the atmosphere, and not to all observers irrespective of their motion. If the careful student goes through the arguments, applying them to sound, he will find that it is not possible to make such general conclusions as the following : " if k is the multiplying factor relating to two observers moving **apart** with uniform speed v, then $1/k$ is the corresponding multiplying factor when they are moving **together** with speed v ". As a matter of fact, with sound, if two observers A and B are moving apart, it matters which one is moving relative to the atmosphere. If A is stationary and sending signals at time intervals t to B who is moving away, B will receive them at some intervals kt. But if B sends signals back to A at intervals t for B, their arrival interval at A is not kt, because the situation is different. B is *moving* and A is not.

From this point of view, sound is a more complicated subject than light, with its simple *law of light*. With light the question never arises " which of the observers is moving ? " There is no ether, and all we need know, for example, is that A and B are moving apart with uniform speed v, i.e., that A is moving with speed v *relative* to B, or that B is moving with speed v relative to A.

relativistic result that time itself must be interpreted as running at a different rate in one system compared to the other.

Suppose, for example, that we go back to our old situation of a space ship moving away from us at speed v. By a pre-arranged plan it has been agreed that this space ship will send us signals at regular intervals, for example, every quarter of an hour, or every hour or every 24 hours. Let us suppose that it has been fixed that a signal will be sent from the space ship every hour. Then we would normally expect the signals to be reaching us at intervals in excess of one hour because of the added distance each successive signal has to travel. Indeed we would expect the signals to be reaching us every $\left(1 + \dfrac{v}{c}\right)$ hours. But, lo and behold, we find that the time interval between the signals reaching us is

$$\text{time interval} = \frac{1 + \dfrac{v}{c}}{\sqrt{1 - \dfrac{v^2}{c^2}}} \text{ hours.}$$

The only way we have of interpreting this is that the space ship's clocks have slowed down so that the space ship is not sending signals every hour at all but at every $\dfrac{1}{\sqrt{1 - \dfrac{v^2}{c^2}}}$ hours. This is the relativity time dilation effect mentioned earlier.

It should be noticed that the time dilation is actually not dependent on whether the ship is travelling away from us or towards us.

Suppose the ship has turned around and is travelling towards us, still sending its signals at the pre-arranged hourly intervals. We would now expect them to be reaching us every $\left(1 - \dfrac{v}{c}\right)$ hours but still they are taking a longer time interval than this ; when we change v into $-v$ in equation (5.17) we see that the time interval between the signals we receive would now be

$$\text{time interval} = \frac{1 - \dfrac{v}{c}}{\sqrt{1 - \dfrac{v^2}{c^2}}} \text{ hours.}$$

Thus to us the space ship's clocks are still running slow by the same factor.

This leads us, as an interesting sidelight, to the famous *Clock Paradox*. Suppose the space ship of our example takes off from earth and goes on a prolonged space voyage. As long as it is going away from us we must assume that its clocks are running slow compared to ours, and similarly on its return voyage the same is still true. Thus when the space ship returns and lands we would have to expect that it has passed through less time than earth has ; the space ship might have been away for five years according to our clocks, but to the space ship's clocks and everybody in the space ship the time of the journey may have been considerably less— say, six months. (We are assuming here that the space ship was actually able to travel quite close to the speed of light). Is such a thing theoretically possible ?

The apparent paradox arises if one imagines one's self on the space ship. To the space traveller the earth is first moving away from him and therefore the time on earth appears to be passing more slowly ; then after he turns around the earth moves back towards him, with its time still travelling more slowly. Would not the space traveller then find that the earth had passed through less time than he had ?

This is a question which we shall not go into in great detail here except to give the answer. It is indeed the first of the above cases which will apply, i.e., that overall the time passed through on the space ship will be less than on earth. This is the conclusion that one reaches as an earth observer, noting that the space ship's time appears to be always running slow. The reason why the second argument is not true is that there is, in fact, an overall difference between the observers on earth and the people who went on the space voyage.

As long as the space ship is drifting with uniform speed away from the earth, the two systems are completely equivalent, and each set of observers would reckon that the time on the other system is running more slowly than their own, and as long as the space ship keeps drifting endlessly through space each set of observers will always keep thinking the same thing. However, in order to return to earth the space ship must subject itself to accelerations of one sort of another, in slowing down or turning around, or in any other manoeuvre. Accelerations can be very obviously felt—particularly accelerations much in excess of that due to gravity on earth—and thus the space travellers do undergo very different experiences in their journey through space and time from the people remaining on earth. A detailed study of this problem in relativity shows that the results obtained by the observers on earth in their " non-accelerated " or so-called " inertial " frame of reference, by which they conclude the space ship's time always runs more slowly, are correct. For the corresponding analysis for a traveller on the space ship, account must be taken of all periods of acceleration in a different way from the simple relativity arguments of this section, which apply to uniform non-accelerated motion only. When a full theoretical analysis is made including the accelerated periods for the space traveller the two results are in agreement, and indeed, the space traveller does find himself younger on his return than his companions on earth.

In principle, therefore, if the technical problems for space travel of being able to achieve speeds close to the speed of light can ever be solved, we will, indeed, have the situation where a space voyager may be away for a few years, and on his return find that the earth has aged 10, or 100, or even 1,000 years depending on how fast he actually travels relative to the earth.

Before we end this Section we should point out that our simple result of equation (5.17) automatically leads to a Doppler effect for light, similar to that for sound—although with the velocity of light being a universal constant, the Doppler effect formula is modified for light.

Suppose a system B is moving away from us with uniform speed v and emitting light. Let us consider one particular spectral line which we know normally has a definite frequency n. Then as far as observers in B are concerned this spectral line will have the frequency n, that is, there will be n complete oscillations of the electro-magnetic field per second of time in B. However, one second of B's time is equal to k seconds of our time, which is more than one second. Thus when the light reaches us it will have n oscillations per k seconds of our time, and thus an actual frequency of n/k per second to us. Let us assume this apparent frequency to us be n' ; thus we have

$$n' = \frac{n}{k} = n \sqrt{\frac{1 - \frac{v}{c}}{1 + \frac{v}{c}}}$$

$$= \frac{n\sqrt{1 - \frac{v^2}{c^2}}}{1 + \frac{v}{c}} \qquad .. \qquad .. \qquad .. \ (5.19)$$

Thus frequencies of spectral lines of light emitted from a system moving away from us become lower and the light is said to be *reddened*. It is from such Doppler shifts that we can determine how fast stars and galaxies are moving away from us.

Similarly, if a system is moving towards us we see the frequencies increased by an amount given by equation (5.19) with v changed to $-v$.

In the Doppler shift equation (5.19) it is the denominator $\left(1 + \frac{v}{c}\right)$ which plays the dominant role until v becomes very close to c. To see this it is useful to know the following approximation when v/c is not too close to unity:*

$$\sqrt{1 - \frac{v^2}{c^2}} \simeq 1 - \frac{1}{2}\frac{v^2}{c^2} \qquad .. \qquad .. \qquad .. \ (5.20a)$$

A similar approximation of equal accuracy is

$$\frac{1}{\sqrt{1 - \frac{v^2}{c^2}}} \simeq 1 + \frac{1}{2}\frac{v^2}{c^2} \qquad .. \qquad .. \qquad .. (5.20b)$$

For a value of $v/c = 0\cdot1$, for example, we have $n' = \frac{n(1 - \cdot005)}{1\cdot1}$. The $\cdot005$ in the numerator is only $\frac{1}{2}$ per cent

---

*The full series expansion for $1 - \frac{v^2}{c^2}$ runs as follows :

$$\sqrt{1 - \frac{v^2}{c^2}} = 1 - \frac{1}{2}\left(\frac{v}{c}\right)^2 - \frac{1}{8}\left(\frac{v}{c}\right)^4 - \frac{1}{16}\left(\frac{v}{c}\right)^6 \quad . \quad . \quad . \quad .$$

It is thus seen that even for $\frac{v}{c} = \frac{1}{2}$ the approximate expression (5.20a) is reasonably accurate, as the next correction term in the series, $\frac{1}{8}\frac{v^4}{c}$, is still only $1/8 \times 1/16 = 1/128$ in magnitude. In fact, you may readily check that with $\frac{v}{c} = \frac{1}{2}$, $\sqrt{1 - \frac{v^2}{c^2}} = \sqrt{\frac{3}{2}} = \cdot866$ to three significant figures. The approximate expression (5.20a) in this case yields $1 - \cdot125 = \cdot875$. Even with $\frac{v}{c} = \frac{1}{2}$ the error in (5.20a) is still only about one per cent., and the formula is progressively much more accurate for smaller v/c. Similar considerations apply to approximation (5.20b).

correction compared to the ten per cent Doppler change due to the $1 \cdot 1$ in the denominator. For such speeds the term $\dfrac{1}{2}\dfrac{v^2}{c^2}$ in the numerator can often be ignored ; this yields the approximate Doppler shift

$$n' \simeq \frac{n}{1 + v/c} \qquad .. \qquad .. \qquad .. \quad (5.21)$$

instead of the full equation (5.19). We will make use of this formula in the next Chapter, although it must be remembered that as v/c approaches unity the full formula (5.19) must be used.

You may notice that although we refer to the possibility of v/c approaching unity we have not referred to the possibility of v/c becoming greater than unity. In fact, it can readily be seen that equation (5.19) then becomes meaningless, since it would include the square root of a negative number. Indeed the theory of relativity tells us that v/c can never exceed or even equal unity. To appreciate this let us return to our situation of an object or observer B moving with uniform speed relative to an observer A, who has previously placed signal boxes distance x apart along B's path. Equation (5.12) gives us the time interval between the light signals which reach A from successive signal boxes when B is travelling towards him. It is from this equation that A would work out B's speed, since A knows at what distance of separation x he places the signal boxes, and he knows c is a universal constant.

If we solve equation (5.12) for v we have

$$v = c\,\frac{x}{x + ct_1} \qquad .. \qquad .. \qquad .. \quad (5.22)$$

This is the equation by which A can calculate the speed with which B is moving towards him. The faster B is travelling towards A the faster he covers each interval x and the smaller the time interval t_1 between two successive signals reaching A. But as t_1 becomes smaller and smaller, tending towards zero, we see that A's estimate of B's speed simply becomes closer to the velocity of light c but will never equal to it, let alone become larger than it. Thus we will never have v/c greater than one.

For this to happen we would actually have to have the t_1 in equation (5.22) negative, i.e., the signals reaching A would be arriving in reverse order to when they were emitted from the signal boxes. In fact the moving object B would be reaching A before the light signals emitted from the various signal boxes.   To see the impossibility of this we can simply realise that we could equally well have the situation that as B passes each signal box a contact of some sort is made which sends out a flash of light from B's own headlight.   This must travel to A at precisely the same speed as the flash from the signal box which is at rest relative to A, since, after all, the speed of light is the same to an observer, completely independent of the motion of the source.   But now the law of light tells us that a flash of light emitted from B's headlight must leave B at the speed of light and therefore will beat B to A.   Thus the light flashes from the signal boxes will automatically be received by A before B arrives. Hence A's determination of B's speed will always give a result less than c.

This is the conclusion of relativity that *nothing can travel faster than the speed of light*, and we will discuss the far-reaching consequences of this statement in the next Chapter.

Another way of reaching the same conclusion is to consider, say, a space ship which has blasted off from earth, and that after appropriate acceleration it is now speeding with uniform velocity away from us.   Suppose we wish to determine its speed relative to us.   The only means we have of doing this is to send out some sort of electro-magnetic radiation signal and to receive a return signal. Now the signal which we send, leaves us with the velocity c, and no matter how powerfully and for what length of time the rocket accelerated and increased its speed away from us, we know that our signal will always catch up on it.   Why ?   Because the *law of light* tells us that the velocity of the electro-magnetic radiation *relative to the space ship* is also c.   The space ship will never " run away " from the signal as can be the case with sound.   If something is travelling in our atmosphere faster than sound it will be impossible to signal to it by means of a sound signal because the sound would never catch up on it.

But in the case of electro-magnetic radiation this is not so. We know that the light or radio signal will overhaul the space ship at a speed which to the occupants will be the constant c.   *Thus we know that our signal will always reach the space ship no matter how fast it is moving away from us.*   Similarly, a reflected or return signal will always return to us. (There will, however, be drastic changes in frequency due to the Doppler effect).

We can only compute the velocity of the space ship on the basis of how long it took our signal to reach the ship and return again. As long as the signal returns we must, of necessity, always attain a value for the speed of the space ship which is *less than the velocity of light*, because we know that our signal actually overtook the space ship. Thus we will *always* attain a speed for the space ship *less than the velocity of light*.

This discussion, of course, does not apply solely to a space ship. If, for example, a small particle is moving very rapidly through some apparatus in the laboratory we can " see " or detect the particle by means of light or electromagnetic radiation produced in the laboratory and reflected from the particle. Exactly the same considerations apply, and we will always obtain a measured speed for the particle less than the velocity of light.

Thus we can understand the statement often popularly described as a prediction of the theory of relativity that *nothing can travel faster than light*. Once again this is not something which is a theoretical prediction from a deep and complicated mathematical theory. It follows automatically from the experimentally established *law of light*.

(e) Addition of Velocities

Another way of concluding that there can be no speed faster than the speed of light is to derive the famous Einstein law for the addition of velocities.

Suppose we consider two observers, B and C, both moving away from an observer A at uniform speeds along the same straight line, with C moving away faster than B. We know that B is moving away from A with speed v_1, say, and that *C is moving away from B at speed v_2*.

What is C's speed away from A? Your first thought may be that it is simply $(v_1 + v_2)$ as it would be in ordinary Newtonian physics. But this is incorrect in relativistic mechanics, as can easily be seen. If we let v be the speed of C away from A, we can solve for v in terms of v_1 and v_2.

Let A transmit signals at time t apart. Then these signals will reach C at a time interval $k_v t$ apart according to his clock, where from equation (5.16) we have

$$k_r = \sqrt{\frac{1 + \dfrac{v}{c}}{1 - \dfrac{v}{c}}} \qquad .. \qquad .. \qquad .. \quad (5.23)$$

Here v is the speed of C away from A (relative to A) for which we wish to solve.

If the above signals are intercepted by B, they arrive at B with a time interval $k_{v1}t$, where

$$k_{v1} = \sqrt{\frac{1 + \dfrac{v_1}{c}}{1 - \dfrac{v_1}{c}}} \qquad .. \qquad .. \qquad .. \quad (5.24)$$

Moreover if B instantaneously re-transmits the signals on to C, then according to C's clocks the time interval is expanded by a further factor k_{v2} over the time interval for B, where again

$$k_{v2} = \sqrt{\frac{1 + \dfrac{v_2}{c}}{1 - \dfrac{v_2}{c}}} \qquad .. \qquad .. \qquad .. \quad (5.25)$$

In this way the time interval at C will be $k_{v1}k_{v2}t$. But since it is irrelevant whether B receives and instantaneously re-transmits the signals or not, this time interval is simply $k_v t$. Thus

$$k_v = k_{v1}k_{v2} \qquad .. \qquad .. \qquad .. \quad (5.26)$$

This is really the famous law for addition of velocities, although it can be expressed in a more familiar form.

If we substitute for k_v, k_{v1} and k_{v2} in (5.26) and square both sides, we have

$$\frac{1 + \dfrac{v}{c}}{1 - \dfrac{v}{c}} = \frac{\left(1 + \dfrac{v_1}{c}\right)\left(1 + \dfrac{v_2}{c}\right)}{\left(1 - \dfrac{v_1}{c}\right)\left(1 - \dfrac{v_2}{c}\right)}$$

If we solve for v we find

$$v = \frac{v_1 + v_2}{1 + \dfrac{v_1 v_2}{c^2}} \qquad .. \qquad .. \qquad .. \qquad .. \quad (5.27)$$

This is the addition of velocities theorem.

For speeds v_1 and v_2 much smaller than c, the term $v_1 v_2/c^2$ in the denominator is negligible and we have $v = v_1 + v_2$. This is the old Newtonian result. But when v_1 and v_2 are close to c the term $v_1 v_2/c^2$ is all important.

Suppose, for example, B is travelling away from A at half the speed of light ($v_1 = c/2$) and then again C is travelling away from B at half the speed of light ($v_2 = c/2$). What is the speed of C away from A (i.e., relative to A)?

From equation (5.27) we have

$$v = \frac{c/2 + c/2}{1 + 1/4} = 4/5c = 0\cdot 8c \qquad .. \qquad .. \quad (5.28)$$

Thus two speeds of $0\cdot 5c$ add together to yield only $0\cdot 8c$.

Similarly, suppose $v_1 = 0\cdot 9c$ and $v_2 = 0\cdot 9c$. We might surely think that when v_1 and v_2 are added together the result is greater than c. But from equation (5.27) we have

$$\frac{v}{c} = \frac{0\cdot 9 + 0\cdot 9}{1 + 0\cdot 81} = \frac{1\cdot 80}{1\cdot 81} \qquad .. \qquad .. \qquad .. \quad (5.29)$$

Thus although v is this time very close to c, the ratio $\dfrac{1\cdot 80}{1\cdot 81}$ is still slightly less than unity, to make v slightly less than c.

Then again if $v_1 = v_2 = 0\cdot 99c$ we have

$$\frac{v}{c} = \frac{0\cdot 99 + 0\cdot 99}{1 + 0\cdot 9801} = \frac{1\cdot 9800}{1\cdot 9801} \qquad .. \qquad .. \qquad .. \quad (5.30)$$

Now v is even very much closer to c, but still slightly less than it.

It is clear, therefore, that no matter how we add velocities together, we can never increase the magnitude of a velocity to exceed the speed of light.

The general law for the addition of many velocities can also easily be derived. Suppose we are " adding together " a series of velocities v_1, v_2, v_3, v_4 - - -. We may imagine the same circumstances as in the above example, with B moving at speed v_1 relative to A, C moving at v_2 relative to B, D with speed v_3 relative to C and so on. What is the speed v of the last observer relative to A? In exactly the same way as in equation (5.26) we have

$$k_v = k_{v1}\, k_{v2}\, k_{v3}\, k_{v4} - - - \quad .. \qquad .. \qquad .. \quad (5.31)$$

and from k_v we immediately know v itself.

CHAPTER 6

Mass and Energy

(a) Mass of the Photon

We saw in Chapter 4 that light is emitted as little packets of energy, which we call *photons*, from individual atoms, and that the energy E contained in each photon is hn, where h is Planck's constant and n is the frequency. Thus when we say that light travels at the same speed relative to all observers, we are saying that each of these little packets of energy or photons is travelling at the same speed c relative to all observers.

We can now use the formulae derived in the last Chapter to show that each photon must be considered to have a certain mass, and we can calculate what this mass is.

Let us consider an atom in which the lowest (ground state) energy of the electrons is E_1 but which has an electron excited into a higher orbit, so that the internal energy in the atom is actually E_2. If this atom decays *at rest*, then the frequency of the emitted photon of radiation is given by

$$hn = E_2 - E_1 \qquad .. \qquad .. \qquad .. \quad (6.1)$$

However, suppose that the excited atom is moving away from an observer with speed v ; its total energy before decaying is therefore its kinetic energy $\frac{1}{2}Mv^2$ where M is the mass of the atom, plus its internal energy E_2. Thus the initial energy of the moving atom with respect to the observer is :

$$\text{Initial Energy} = \tfrac{1}{2}Mv^2 + E_2 \qquad .. \qquad .. \quad (6.2)$$

Suppose the atom now decays by firing its photon back towards the observer. We know that the observer must see this photon not with frequency n as given by equation (6.1) but with the Doppler shift frequency n' discussed in the previous Chapter. Thus to the observer the emitted photon only has energy hn'. To be general we can suppose that as the photon is emitted backwards it gives the atom a kick and increases its speed a little from v to v'.

Thus after the photon is emitted the energy of the system is

$$\text{Final Energy} = \tfrac{1}{2}Mv'^2 + E_1 + hn' \qquad .. \qquad .. \quad (6.3)$$

By conservation of energy we must have that equations (6.2) and (6.3) are equal. If we re-arrange terms we find

$$\tfrac{1}{2}M(v'^2 - v^2) = E_2 - E_1 - hn'$$

$$= h(n - n') \quad .. \quad .. \quad .. \quad (6.4)$$

One immediate conclusion can be reached from this equation ; we know that n' must be different from n by the discussion of the last Chapter. For, after all, n is the frequency as seen by an observer moving with the atom and n' is different because of the Doppler shift. Thus v' must also be different from v, i.e., the velocity of the atom must change slightly. From energy conservation alone we cannot say any more ; but there is another well-known conservation law which must also be satisfied—conservation of momentum. And from this we know immediately that the photon must have a certain momentum —say p. For if it did not, conservation of momentum would show that the momentum of the atom would be the same before and after the emission of the photon—i.e., we would have $Mv = Mv'$ and hence, from equation (6.4), $n = n'$ which is in contradiction to the fact that we know on general grounds that there must be a Doppler shift.

Thus we must allow that the photon carries off momentum p, which we can now calculate. Conservation of momentum yields the equation

$$Mv = Mv' - p \quad .. \quad .. \quad .. \quad (6.5)$$

If we use this equation to eliminate v' from (6.4) we obtain the equation

$$\frac{p^2}{2M} + vp - h(n - n') = 0 \quad .. \quad .. \quad (6.6)$$

If we solve this equation for p we obtain the result

$$p = M \left[-v \pm \sqrt{v^2 + \frac{2h(n - n')}{M}} \right] \quad .. \quad (6.7)$$

You may easily verify that with either $+$ or $-$ sign in front of the square root this value for p satisfies equation (6.6) ; as a matter of fact, however, we must use the $+$ sign in front of the square root in order to obtain p positive which it must be.
Hence we have

$$p = M \left[-v + v\sqrt{1 + \frac{2h(n - n')}{Mv^2}} \right] \quad .. \quad (6.8)$$

It should be noticed that the second term under the square root has a $1/M$ factor ; and although we have discussed the problem for a particular atom emitting the photon, M can really be imagined as large as we like. For the atom may be simply one of a very large number of atoms in a body which is travelling with speed v ; if the atom is bound in a piece of solid material, for example, the mass M should be more like that of the entire material. Thus since we can really imagine M to be as large as we like, the second term under the square root could be considered much smaller than unity. We can, therefore, very accurately use approximation (5.20a) for the square root, in which case the mass M disappears entirely from the expression (6.8), and we have the simple result

$$p = \frac{h(n - n')}{v} \qquad \dots \quad \dots \quad \dots \quad (6.9)$$

From Chapter 5 we know what the connection between n and n' must be ; this is given by equation (5.19), or for not too large values of v/c by equation (5.21). If we employ equation (5.21) for simplicity we have $n = n'\left(1 + \dfrac{v}{c}\right)$. On substituting this in (6·9) we have simply

$$p = \frac{hn'}{c} \qquad \dots \quad \dots \quad \dots \quad (6.10)$$

Thus we see that with a photon with frequency n' with respect to a certain observer, and energy hn', it must also be considered to have momentum $\dfrac{hn'}{c}$. But this means that it must also be considered to have mass $\dfrac{hn'}{c^2}$, since *momentum* is *mass* multiplied by *speed* and the speed is the velocity of light c.

Thus we arrive at the important and general conclusion that **a photon of frequency n to a certain observer, must be considered by that observer not only to have energy hn, but momentum $\dfrac{hn}{c}$ and mass $\dfrac{hn}{c^2}$.**

Thus even though there is no matter involved at all, and a photon really consists of a short burst of oscillating electric and magnetic fields propagating with velocity c, nevertheless we now see it must have an equivalent mass $\dfrac{hn}{c^2}$ where n is its frequency.

It has indeed confirmed that this is the case, and for many discussions it is completely adequate for us to think of a beam of light of frequency n simply as a beam of particles, the photons moving with velocity c. Of course, the mass of each of these photons is extremely small because of the very large value of c^2 in the denominator. For example, light of wave-length 5,000A° has a frequency $n = \frac{c}{\lambda}$. The equivalent mass m of the photons making up this radiation is thus

$$m = \frac{h}{c\lambda} = \frac{6 \cdot 5 \times 10^{-27}}{3 \times 10^{10} \times 5 \times 10^{-5}}$$

$$\simeq 4 \cdot 3 \times 10^{-33} \ g.$$

This is indeed a very small mass. Yet the picture of light consisting of a beam of actual particles with a mass determined by the frequency is an extremely useful one which can be employed in many discussions on light. The only cases for which we must delve deeper and use the actual wave character of light are those in which interference effects are involved.

Small as the mass of a photon is, it can actually be detected experimentally by the method in Figure 6.1. Light from a distant star is observed from a point on the earth at such a time that the light rays just " graze " the sun. These rays can be clearly seen if at the same time the sun is undergoing a total eclipse at the point of observation—i.e., if the moon is exactly between the observer and the sun, so that the observing apparatus is not " blinded " by the sun's direct rays.

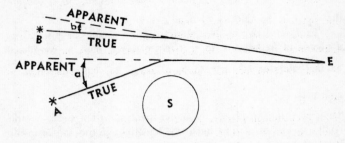

FIGURE 6.1

Light rays are bent towards the sun by the sun's gravitational field. Light from star A is deviated through some angle a. This is greater, for example, than the angle of deviation b for rays from B which do not pass so close to the sun.

The light rays from the distant star, being made up of photons with effective mass, are actually bent by the gravitational attraction to the sun as they pass it, and thus the star appears to be in a different location in the sky from its true location. By observing the change in the star's position produced by the sun, it is possible to measure the gravitational deflection of the sun's rays. Such deflection has been experimentally measured on numerous occasions : by this and many other observations it has clearly been established that photons do have an equivalent mass $\frac{hn}{c^2}$.

We can illustrate the usefulness of the concept of a light beam as a stream of particles by a discussion of what is called radiation pressure. It is well known that when light falls on a surface which is a good reflector (shiny surface, e.g., a mirror), the light is nearly all reflected. This means that the photons bounce off the reflecting surface just as particles suffering perfectly elastic collisions with a wall. If the beam of light is directed at right angles to the surface, the photons are reflected straight back along their incident path. Just as atoms of a gas bouncing off the walls of a container provide a pressure on the walls, so therefore we would expect a beam of light being reflected from a surface to produce a pressure on that surface, because in this case the " photon particles " are bouncing off the surface.

Consider, for example, a beam of light of intensity I ; this means that I is the amount of incident energy passing per second through unit area at right angles to the beam. If the frequency of the light is n, we therefore have that

$$I = Nhn \qquad .. \qquad .. \qquad .. \quad (6.11)$$

where N is the number of photons passing per second through unit area at right angles to the beam.

The momentum of each photon is $\frac{hn}{c}$, and when the surface is reflecting each photon is bounced back in the opposite direction. The total change in momentum per photon is then $2\frac{hn}{c}$. Hence the total change in momentum imparted per second to photons hitting unit area of the reflecting surface is

$$\text{Total momentum change/second} = \frac{2Nhn}{c} = \frac{2\,I}{c} \quad .. \quad (6.12)$$

But change in momentum *per second* per unit area is precisely the pressure exerted on the reflecting surface. Thus we have

$$\text{radiation pressure} = \frac{2\,I}{c} \quad .. \quad .. \quad .. \quad (6.13)$$

This radiation pressure has been observed experimentally in many cases. In fact, it may provide the explanation of an effect which has been observed for many hundred of years. It is well known that the solar system contains a large number of comets, which are travelling in highly elliptical orbits around the sum. About 40 comets are known, with periods ranging from between 10 and 1000 years. Perhaps the most famous is Halley's comet, which last came close to the sun and was visible from earth in 1910 and is due to return in 1984.

When such a comet comes in close to the sun it develops a long, bright tail *which always points away from the sun*.

Comets have very large dimensions, the main head being any-thing from 50,000 to 200,000 miles across, and when it forms, the tail may be anything from 5,000,000 to 50,000,000 miles in length. Yet the mass of a typical comet (estimated from the perturbing effects of comets on a planet's orbit) is extremely small—at most a few thousand million tons—indicating that the comet's average density is what we would call a good vacuum in the laboratory. The tails, and even the heads, are relatively transparent and do not noticeably dim the light of stars seen through them. It seems that the head of a comet is a loose assembly of small particles of solid metallic nature—like a swarm of bees flying along—and between these parts are frozen gases, such as icy lumps of ammonia.

When such a comet approaches close to the sun the frozen gases volatilize and stream out " behind " the comet. It is not really true to say, however, that they stream behind the planet. but rather that they are " blown " away by the radiation pressure of the light from the sun. This is why the tails are always observed to be pointing directly away from the sun—simply because it is from the sun that the radiation " wind " is coming.

It is this same radiation pressure that may one day be useful in space travel. It makes possible what has been popularly termed " sailing by sunlight " as a way of utilizing the sun's rays as a means of propulsion. This is illustrated in Figure 6.2.

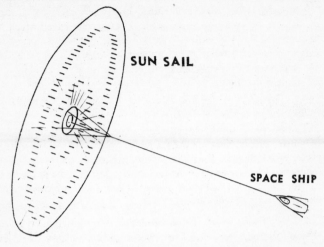

FIGURE 6·2
" *Sailing* " *by sunlight.*

Another interesting example of the effects of radiation pressure is given by the fact that one of the first American earth satellites (which had a mass of about 10 pounds), developed significant deviations from its predicted orbit due to the continued effects of radiation pressure.

Apart from such large scale observation as with comets. however, the formula (6.13) has been very accurately verified in the laboratory.

It is to be noticed that the derivation depended on the assumption that the light is essentially all reflected, e.g., that the surface formed a perfect reflector. Actually there can be surfaces which appear black and which thus absorb the radiation that falls on them. converting the energy into heat motion of its atoms. Such a surface is said to be a good absorber of radiation. In this case the momentum change of each photon is simply $\dfrac{hn}{c}$, since each photon is merely stopped and not reflected back on its tracks. In this event the total radiation pressure is simply $\dfrac{I}{c}$, i.e., is a factor of two less than in equation (6.13).

Another effect which illustrates very clearly the particle aspect of light is the photo-electric effect. This is an effect which was first noticed by Hertz in his work on the production of electro-magnetic waves. What Hertz noticed was that the air in a spark gap became a better conductor of electricity when it was illuminated by ultra-violet light. Hallwachs (1888) also found that a zinc surface which was charged negatively would lose its charge very rapidly when illuminated by ultra-violet light.

Many other similar experiments were also performed and were, of course, understood once the Rutherford picture of the atom became established. It was clear that bombardment of atoms by electro-magnetic radiation could result in an ionization of some of the atoms. In other words, the radiation was capable of knocking outer satellite electrons out of the atoms.

This effect is called the photo-electric effect and can be particu-larly understood in terms of the photon picture of light. Consider, for example, the simple case of an assembly of hydrogen atoms being bombarded by electromagnetic radiation of a certain fre-quency n. We may, therefore, look upon the light as a stream of photons, each of energy hn and of mass $\dfrac{hn}{c^2}$. These photons are, of course, made up of a wave packet of electric and magnetic fields and will certainly produce a force on the atomic electrons of the hydrogen atoms, if they are close enough. Thus we may picture the photons as being able to " collide " with the atomic electrons. In any such collision the electron may be " knocked up " to an excited state in the atoms, and the photon loses energy in the process— i.e., it becomes a photon of a lower frequency.

If, however, the original energy hn of the bombarding photons is sufficiently large, it is possible that in some cases they will succeed in knocking electrons completely out of the atoms altogether— in other words, the bombarding photons will be capable of ionizing some of the hydrogen atoms. In such cases the liberated electrons will escape from the parent atoms with positive kinetic energy. The maximum kinetic energy which any such electron can have comes from a collision in which the bombarding photon essentially loses all its energy and imparts it entirely to the electron with which it collided.

It is to be noticed that this maximum kinetic energy on the liberated electrons is in no way dependent on the actual intensity of the bombarding radiation, but simply on its frequency. This was an effect which was observed experimentally in the early experiments on the photo-electric effect and was, at first, considered very difficult to understand. This effect was first explained by Einstein, using the above photon picture.

Of course, this photo-electric effect can occur with any substance, not simply with hydrogen atoms. If the surface of a solid, for example, is illuminated with radiation, the photons of the radiation will make collisions with electrons in atoms near the surface. If the frequency of the radiation is sufficiently high, there will, in fact, be some electrons which are knocked out of the surface entirely. This is the effect which Hallwachs observed. Once again, the maximum kinetic energy which the electrons will have on escaping from the solid depends entirely on the frequency of the radiation, not on its intensity. The intensity—i.e., the number of photons in the bombarding radiation—determines the number of electrons that are knocked out, but not their energies.

Just as in the case of thermionic emission, this photo-electric effect has become of extreme importance practically. The fact that electrons can be liberated when a solid substance is heated has given rise to the vacuum tubes. Similarly, the photo-electric effect has been used in the production of what is called a phototube. This is an evacuated tube as in the case of the ordinary electronic valve with a cathode and an anode between which an electrical potential difference is maintained. Normally, however, no current can flow, because the cathode is not heated. However, the cathode has a surface consisting of a material which is said to be " photo sensitive "—i.e., one from which relatively low frequency photons liberate electrons. If light is allowed to fall on a cathode, electrons are liberated and a current flows through the tube.

In this way it is possible to detect extremely weak light signals and to convert them into electric currents which can be amplified by means of a normal electronic amplifier. Such photo-tubes are of very great use both practically and in scientific research.

(b) Mass and Energy

The fact that photons have mass immediately yields a very famous result called the **Einstein Mass-Energy Relationship.** Consider some material of mass M at rest in the laboratory. Suppose we now heat this material so that it glows red hot, perhaps even white hot ; in other words, the material is emitting light or sending off photons. Consider what happens after a very large number of, say, N photons of frequency n have been emitted ; these will have been emitted in equal numbers in all directions so that the material is still at rest in the laboratory. **But they will have carried away a total mass equal to** Nhn/c^2. If, for example, we consider light of wave-length 5,000A°, approximately 2×10^{32} photons will carry away a mass of one gram.

Thus as photons are emitted from a material, *so they carry away mass*, and we can only conclude that the mass of the material is diminishing. In fact, if a total energy E is carried away by all the photons the mass of the material must have decreased by an amount E/c^2.

We must in turn conclude that when an amount of energy E in any form is added to the material its *mass increases* by an amount E/c^2. In our example above suppose the material initially has mass M_0. We then heated it, which means simply that we supplied energy which increased the kinetic energy of movement of the atoms of the material themselves, and also increased the average energy (kinetic + potential) of the electrons within each atom. Thus the energy added to the material—say, E—which simply raised the kinetic and potential energies of the atoms within the material, **must have increased the mass of the material from** M_0 **to a value** $M = M_0 + \dfrac{E}{c_2}$. For when this energy is radiated away in the form of photons these carry away the mass E/c^2 and the mass of material drops to its original value M_0.

Thus when we add an amount of energy E to an object this amount of energy is completely specified by stating it in terms of the increase in mass of the object. We thus arrive at the famous conclusion of Einstein that an amount of energy E must have a mass m given by

$$E = mc^2 \qquad .. \qquad .. \qquad .. \quad (6.14)$$

and even an object of mass M in the laboratory must be thought of as containing an energy Mc^2 ; when the mass drops to a lower value M_0 an amount of energy $(M - M_0)c^2$ is always given off. If the matter could ever be made to disappear entirely, the equivalent energy Mc^2 would have to appear entirely in some other form, e.g., by the emission of electro-magnetic radiation.

One of the most well-known applications of this energy mass equivalence is in the production of nuclear energy in which a uranium nucleus undergoes what is called **fission**. If a U^{235} nucleus is bombarded by a slow neutron it breaks into two separate nuclei each containing in the vicinity of half the particles of the original uranium nucleus. A few loose neutrons are usually left over and it is these that make a chain reaction possible because they can go on and produce fission in neighbouring uranium nuclei. The point is that in any one fission process the sum of the masses of the uranium nucleus plus neutron before the process is greater than the sum of the masses of the final products. The mass difference appears as energy in the form mainly of violent kinetic energy of separation of the two final nuclear fragments.

When an object of mass M_0 is sitting at rest in the laboratory the energy M_0c^2 is said to be its "rest energy". We have seen that if we add energy to this object this can be completely expressed by saying that the mass increases to a value M where $(M - M_0)c^2$ is the amount of energy added. Now suppose the energy added is not in the form of heat energy but is simply such as to make the object move through the laboratory with a velocity v, i.e., we accelerate the object by means of a force to some speed v and thereby give it kinetic energy. We have seen that we should be able to express this simply by saying that the object now has a higher mass M and energy Mc^2, where the difference $(M - M_0)c^2$ is the kinetic energy we have supplied to the object.

But if an object has mass M_0 when at rest and we accelerate the object to a speed v, we normally, following Newton's laws, say that the kinetic energy is $\frac{1}{2}M_0v^2$. On this basis we would have to say that the energy added $(M - M_0)c^2 = \frac{1}{2}M_0v^2$. This would tell us that the new mass M is given by :

$$M = M_0\left(1 + \frac{1}{2}\frac{v^2}{c^2}\right) \qquad .. \qquad .. \qquad .. \quad (6.15)$$

While this is indeed very accurate for all speeds such that v/c is not too large, Einstein showed that Newton's laws are really making use of our approximation (5.20b) and that strictly the new mass of the moving object moving relative to an observer with speed v is

$$M = \frac{M_0}{\sqrt{1 - v^2/c^2}} \qquad .. \quad .. \quad .. \quad (6.16)$$

Thus Einstein's Theory of Relativity corrects Newton's laws, by a correction which only matters for speeds very close to the speed of light. We now say that an object at rest with mass M_0 has rest mass energy $M_0 c^2$. If work is done on the object to accelerate it to a speed v its energy becomes

$$Mc^2 = \frac{M_0 c^2}{\sqrt{1 - v^2/c^2}} \qquad .. \quad .. \quad .. \quad (6.17)$$

The increase in energy, which in this case is the kinetic energy of the moving object, is strictly

$$\text{Kinetic Energy} = (M - M_0)c^2 = M_0 c^2 \left\{ \frac{1}{\sqrt{1 - v^2/c^2}} - 1 \right\}$$

$$.. \quad .. \quad .. \quad (6.18)$$

Whenever approximation (5.20b) can be used this reduces to our normal Newtonian formula for the kinetic energy.

These considerations fit in completely with our observation of the previous Chapter that nothing can travel faster than light. At first sight this would seem an absurdity since we can imagine applying an accelerating force to an object and by doing work on it accelerate it to indefinitely high speeds. Since the true kinetic energy of the moving object is, however, that given by equation (6.18) we see that this can become as large as we like as v gets nearer and nearer to c, and that v will never have to exceed c. In fact, the work being done on the object simply goes into increasing the mass more and more and making the speed become closer and closer to the speed of light without ever exceeding or even being equal to it.

Finally, we should perhaps comment on the fact that when we calculated the mass of the photon in *Section (a)* of this Chapter, we actually used the Newtonian approximation for the kinetic energy of the moving atom. Is our result, that the mass of a photon of frequency $n = hn/c^2$, therefore an approximation? No! You may recall that we also used the low speed approximation for the Doppler shift (Equation 5.21) and this actually just cancels the above small error. When we use the full relativistic discussion for conserving energy and momentum—with the momentum of the moving object being $Mv = \dfrac{M_0 v}{\sqrt{1 - v^2/c^2}}$ and use the exact Doppler effect formula (equation 5.19), we obtain precisely the same result for the momentum and mass of the photon.

(c) Exact Calculation*

The fact that the mass of a photon of frequency n is indeed hn/c^2, and that the mass of an object moving with speed v is

$$M = \frac{M_0}{\sqrt{1 - v^2/c^2}}$$

where M_0 is its rest mass, can be shown from an accurate consideration of energy and momentum balance.

Let us re-do the example in part (a) of this Chapter exactly, assuming that the above are correct. We can show that we do indeed reproduce precisely the correct Doppler shift formula (5.19).

We consider the emission of a photon by an atom contained in an object of rest mass M_0. When the atom is in its excited state the mass of the object is $M_0{}^*$, and the frequency n of the photon emitted when the atom decays to its ground state is given by

$$nh = (M_0{}^* - M_0)\, c^2 \qquad .. \qquad .. \quad (6.19)$$

Suppose now the atom is initially moving away from an observer at speed v, in its excited state. The total initial energy of the moving atom with respect to the observer is

$$\text{Initial energy} = \frac{M_0{}^* c^2}{\sqrt{1 - v^2/c^2}} \qquad .. \qquad .. \quad (6.20)$$

The atom decays by firing its photon back towards the observer—but with apparent frequency n' rather than n : the atom's speed

---

*The reading of this section can be postponed by those who find it difficult.

increases a little to v'. The total energy of the system after firing is

$$\text{Final energy} = \frac{M_0 c^2}{\sqrt{1 - v'^2/c^2}} + nh' \qquad \text{.. (6.21)}$$

By conservation of energy we have

$$\frac{M_0{}^* c^2}{\sqrt{1 - v^2/c^2}} = \frac{M_0 c^2}{\sqrt{1 - v'^2/c^2}} + hn' \qquad \text{..} \qquad \text{.. (6.22)}$$

If we employ equation (6.14) to eliminate $M_0{}^*$ we obtain the result

$$hn' = \frac{hn}{\sqrt{1 - v^2/c^2}} + \frac{M_0 c^2}{\sqrt{1 - v^2/c^2}} - \frac{M_0 c^2}{\sqrt{1 - v'^2/c^2}} \qquad \text{.. (6.23)}$$

It is useful to rewrite

$$\frac{1}{\sqrt{1 - v'^2/c^2}} = \frac{1}{\sqrt{1 - v^2/c^2 + \dfrac{v^2 - v'^2}{c^2}}}$$

$$= \frac{1}{\sqrt{1 - v^2/c^2}} \times \frac{1}{\sqrt{1 - \dfrac{v'^2 - v^2}{c^2 - v^2}}} \qquad \text{..} \qquad \text{.. (6.24)}$$

     Now v and v' are very nearly equal, and as M_0 is made larger and larger, $(v' - v)$ becomes smaller and smaller. Since we can make M_0 as large as we like we can make $(v' - v)$ as small as we like. It is then quite rigorously accurate to use the representation (5.20b) for the second square-root factor of (6.24), so that

$$\frac{1}{\sqrt{1 - v'^2/c^2}} = \frac{1}{\sqrt{1 - v^2/c^2}} \left\{ 1 + \tfrac{1}{2} \frac{v'^2 - v^2}{c^2 - v^2} \right\} \qquad \text{.. (6.25)}$$

Hence the energy conservation equation (6.23) becomes

$$hn' = \frac{hn}{\sqrt{1 - v^2/c^2}} - \frac{M_0 c^2}{\sqrt{1 - v^2/c^2}} \left\{ \frac{1}{2} \frac{v'^2 - v^2}{c^2 - v^2} \right\}$$

$$= \frac{hn}{\sqrt{1 - v^2/c^2}} - \frac{M_0 c^2}{\sqrt{1 - v^2/c^2}} \left\{ \frac{(v' + v)(v' - v)}{2(c^2 - v^2)} \right\}$$

But as M_0 becomes larger and larger $v' + v$ simply tends to $2v$; we can therefore just replace $v' + v$ by $2v$. We must be careful to leave $v' - v$, however, since as yet we do not know what the product $M_0 c^2 (v' - v)$ will be as M_0 tends to infinity and $v' - v$ tends to zero.

The energy conservation equation thus finally reads

$$hn' = \frac{hn}{\sqrt{1 - v^2/c^2}} - \frac{M_0 c^2}{\sqrt{1 - v^2/c^2}} \left\{ \frac{v(v' - v)}{c^2 - v^2} \right\} \qquad .. \ (6.26)$$

Conservation of momentum yields the equation

$$\frac{M_0{}^* v}{\sqrt{1 - v^2/c^2}} = \frac{M_0 v'}{\sqrt{1 - v'^2/c^2}} - \frac{hn'}{c} \qquad .. \qquad .. \ (6.27)$$

From equation (6.19) we can rewrite this as

$$- hn' = \frac{hn \, v/c}{\sqrt{1 - v^2/c^2}} + \frac{M_0 vc}{\sqrt{1 - v^2/c^2}} - \frac{M_0 v'c}{\sqrt{1 - v'^2/c^2}}$$

and then again by using (6.25) we obtain

$$- hn' = \frac{hn \, v/c}{\sqrt{1 - v^2/c^2}} + \frac{M_0 c^2}{\sqrt{1 - v^2/c^2}} \left[\frac{v}{c} - \frac{v'}{c} \left\{ 1 + \frac{1}{2} \frac{v'^2 - v^2}{c^2 - v^2} \right\} \right]$$

$$= \frac{hn \, v/c}{\sqrt{1 - v^2/c^2}} - \frac{M_0 c^2}{\sqrt{1 - v^2/c^2}} \left[\frac{v' - v}{c} + \frac{1}{2} \frac{v'}{c} \frac{(v' - v)(v' + v)}{c^2 - v^2} \right]$$

If we again remember that we can let $v' \to v$ in the right hand side except when in the difference $(v' - v)$ we finally obtain the result

$$- hn' = \frac{hn \, v/c}{\sqrt{1 - v^2/c^2}} - \frac{M_0 c^2}{\sqrt{1 - v^2/c^2}} \cdot \frac{c(v' - v)}{c^2 - v^2} \qquad .. \ (6.28)$$

We can now eliminate the unknown product $M_0c^2(v' - v)$ from equations (6.26) and (6.28). If we multiply (6.28) by v/c and subtract from (6.26) we find

$$hn' \left(1 + v/c = \frac{hn}{\sqrt{1 - v^2/c^2}} (1 - v^2/c^2)\right.$$

Thus

$$n' = \frac{n(1 - v/c)}{\sqrt{1 - v^2/c^2}} = n \sqrt{\frac{1 - v/c}{1 + v/c}} \qquad .. \qquad .. \quad (6.29)$$

This is precisely the true result (equation (5.19)) which was derived in Chapter 5 on general grounds from the law of light. We have here derived it again from the assumption that the total energy of a moving object of rest mass M_0 is $\dfrac{M_0c^2}{\sqrt{1 - v^2/c^2}}$ with v being its speed, and that the energy and momentum of a photon of frequency n is hn and hn/c respectively. The mass of the photon (speed c) must follow as hn/c^2.

RELATIVITY
AND TIME

by

H. BONDI

H. BONDI
Professor of Applied Mathematics, King's College,
University of London.

CHAPTER 1

Relativity

An examination of the roots of the time concept was undertaken by E. A. Milne in the mid nineteen-thirties. He based on it a system of cosmology ("Kinematic Relativity") which has by now been largely forgotten for a variety of reasons, but his analysis of time is still of great value.

He starts with the notion that the only aspect of time of which one is immediately and directly aware is its passage, i.e. the relevance of the words "before", "now", "after" to events happening at one's own location. At this stage there is no measurement of the length of intervals of time; all that time does is to order local events into a sequence. Just as one can gain insight into geometry by omitting all consideration of lengths and angles ("projective geometry") so one appreciates the nature of time better if one contemplates this simple situation, for then *any* method of correlating one's sequence of experiences with the sequence of real numbers can be called a clock, provided only that the experience corresponding to a higher number is always to be regarded as later than the experience corresponding to a lower number.

There are innumerable different such systems, different clocks, expanding or contracting relative to each other's time intervals at different stages but never inverting the order of events. As soon as one has a clock one can employ it not only to measure times, but also distances. For this purpose one uses *radar,* a device familiar from military and civil applications at airports, etc., in which a pulse of radiation (light, radio waves, etc.) is sent out and some of it, scattered by the target, is later received back. The time interval between transmission and reception, as measured by one's clock, defines the distance of the target. Distance is then not measured in yards or centimetres but in intervals of *time.* This is familiar from astronomy, where one speaks of the *light year* as unit, that is the distance travelled by light in a year. This method of measuring distances has the great advantage of dispersing with the concept of the rigid ruler which, with its myriad interlacing atoms, is a highly complicated tool to analyze. Moreover, it has the advantage of making a very fundamental quantity, the speed of light, equal to one (by definition). Evidently light travels at such a speed that it covers the distance of a light year, in one year. for if it did otherwise that distance would not be called a light year. Viewed in this (fundamental and useful) manner, the value of the speed of light (one) is wholly based on definition and not on experiment, just like, say, the number of inches in one foot (twelve) is so by definition and not as the result of careful measurement. Radar, incidentally, is now of great scientific importance, since the distance to the Moon and to Venus is known more accurately through radar than by any other means, as are some distances on the Earth. When Milne developed his analysis, thirty years ago, he did so as pure theory before the first radar set was constructed.

If people use different clocks (in the sense indicated, so that the reading of one may be any steadily increasing function of the readings of the others) they will therefore get very different pictures of the world both in time and in space. An object that, with one of the clocks, appears to be approaching with constant speed, may be regarded as standing still with another, as receding with high acceleration with a third one, etc. One's entire view of the universe will therefore depend on one's choice of clock. It would be absurd to regard one kind of clock as "right" and another as "wrong" since one cannot take a second, as measured by a clock one day, and lay it along a second measured by that clock some other day, to test whether they are the same. It may, however, turn out that some kinds of clock are more convenient to use or easier to construct than others.

In practice we seem to be able to work with three quite different types of clock, gravitational, atomic and nuclear. An example of a gravitational clock is given by the motion of the Earth round the Sun. Owing to the force of gravitation, this is a periodic motion, giving us the *year* as unit of time. A very usual kind of atomic clock is a wrist watch, in which the "tick rate" is controlled by the interatomic forces giving the hair-spring its strength. A more accurate and recondite kind of atomic clock is the caesium clock, an elaborate piece of laboratory apparatus in which the tick rate is controlled by an internal vibration of the caesium atom. A nuclear clock is one controlled by the decay of some radio-active material. We have reasonable grounds for supposing that all gravitational clocks keep the same time among themselves and similarly for atomic clocks, though there might be more than one kind of nuclear clock. On the other hand we have no sure knowledge that an atomic clock always keeps the same time as a nuclear or a gravitational clock. It is conceivable, for example, that whereas half of a quantity of radium now decays in 1,628 revolutions of the Earth about the Sun, 1,000 million years ago radium might have decayed to the same extent only in 2,000 such revolutions. Indeed Milne based much of his theory of the universe on the concept of such different time scales. Ideas of this sort are now not much in favour, but we must reckon with such an elasticity of the time concept, even if only to discard it. No physical quantity has more or wider reality than is given to it by the method of measuring it, and if there are fundamentally different means of measuring such a quantity, as is the case with time, the possibility of the entire concept disintegrating into an atomic time, a nuclear time and a gravitational time must be faced, even if it is not pursued.

The chief reason why the idea of different time-scales is not favoured is that it is not very fertile and does not seem to solve many problems. Also it involves an explicit denial of the homogeneity of time, the notion that all moments are equally good, that the past does not basically differ from the present or the future, just as the homogeniety of space is the notion that all positions in space are equivalent. Connected with these ideas is the fundamental idea of Newton that all velocities are equivalent and that velocity by itself cannot be appreciated. Only in this way can we accept the Copernican system since the velocity of the Earth in its orbit is not directly noticed by us. Newton's theory of the irrelevancy of velocity was eventually given its logical completion by Einstein with his *special theory of relativity*. This theory has greatly deepened our understanding of the nature of time and will therefore be described next.

The theory has its basis in Newton's first law of dynamics, the law of inertia, which states that a body on which no forces act moves in a straight line with constant velocity. This law, based on Galileo's researches, was a total reversal of the attitude of the ancients, who thought that a force was required to *maintain* a body in motion, whereas Newton's laws state a force is only required if the velocity is *changed*. The picture of the ancients is indeed a rational extrapolation of our experience that all motion in our neighbourhood (such as a ball rolling on level ground) will come to rest, unless a force continues to be applied. However, the picture broke down when it was attempted to apply it to the Moon and the planets, for they keep on moving without a visible force maintaining their motion. It was Newton's genius to realize that the coming to rest in our vicinity, although so familiar, constitutes a complicated interplay of such forces as friction and air resistance, while the seemingly strange behaviour of the Moon and the planets admitted of a simple description.

In the Newtonian system, a force is something highly tangible, like a rope pulling a body. The first law therefore consists in noting that whenever a body is moving without acceleration (i.e. without its velocity changing in magnitude or direction) then no rope is found to be pulling the body, whereas whenever there is acceleration, then a rope will be found to be tugging at the body. [N.B. In this and the next chapter we shall suppose the least tangible of all forces, gravitation, to be absent, and shall examine this very special force later.] We can now ask which observer will find, in their personal experience, Newton's first law to be correct. As an example of an observer who does not find it to be correct, consider a man riding on an empty bus watching a ball resting on the floor. If the driver applies the brake hard, the ball will begin to move forward without there being a rope present, so that this observer will not agree that Newton's first law applies. On the other hand, if we start with an observer who finds the law to be correct, then any other observer moving relative to this one with constant velocity will agree with him on which bodies are and which are not accelerated, since the addition of a constant velocity to a constant velocity results in a constant velocity. Thus all such observers find the first law, the law of inertia, to be correct and thus we call any such observer an *inertial observer*. Hence the relative motion of any two inertial observers is a velocity constant in magnitude and direction. Any differently moving observer, accelerated relative to an inertial observer, will not agree to Newton's first law and is thus called *non-inertial*.

It is clear that, by definition, all inertial observers are equivalent as far as the law of inertia is concerned because this is how we picked them out. In Newton's second law, force is put equal to mass times acceleration. It is not logically compelling but highly plausible that, through suitably measuring the expressions occurring in Newton's second law, inertial observers are also equivalent as far as this law is concerned. Since all dynamics is based on these two laws, it follows that *all inertial observers are equivalent as far as dynamical experiments are concerned.* This very important statement is called *Newton's principle of relativity* and we can make its meaning clear by considering a few examples. We cannot appreciate the velocity of the Earth in its orbit round the Sun in spite of its great magnitude (19 miles per second or 68,000 m.p.h.) because all dynamical processes occur equally on all inertial observers, i.e., they are independent of velocity. To take another case, imagine a super-airliner of the future, very fast, so well soundproofed that passengers cannot hear the engines at all, and without windows and very smooth in flight. A passenger on a long distance flight who falls asleep and wakes up wondering whether he is still hurtling along at colossal speed or whether the airliner has stopped at some intermediate airfield cannot tell by listening for the engine noise, as the engines cannot be heard anyway, nor can he tell by looking out of the window, as there are none. By virtue of Newton's principle of relativity he cannot tell either by performing a dynamical experiment such as pouring out a cup of coffee, for the coffee will pour in just the same way whether the plane is at rest on the ground or moving at constant speed.

Thus Newton's principle of relativity asserts that velocity is purely relative and thus irrelevant for dynamics. On the other hand, the reality of force shows clearly that acceleration is regarded as absolute.

The Newtonian system can be criticised for its narrowness in concentrating on dynamics. For dynamics is but a text book division of physics, which is a subject possessing a tremendous degree of unity and coherence. One can no more have an experiment in pure dynamics, with no other branch of physics coming in, than one can have an experiment in pure optics or pure heat. In a dynamical experiment, materials are always involved with a structure determined by quantal interatomic electro-magnetic forces, light is used to observe the experiment, etc. All the branches of physics are inseparably intertwined. Hence a statement like Newton's principle of relativity, with its restriction to dynamics, is logically an empty statement since there is no purely dynamical experiment. Since the statement corresponds to something in our experience. as in the example of the airliner, the suspicion arises that the restriction to dynamics is entirely due to the method of derivation since this is based on the laws of dynamics. It is therefore a reasonable and plausible hypothesis that the restriction is unnecessary so that the principle should simply read:

All inertial observers are equivalent.

This statement is known as *Einstein's principle of relativity.* Since it is only proposed as a hypothesis it is necessary to test it. This can be done only by deriving experimentally relevant consequences of it, and performing the experiments suggested. These derivations will be carried out in the next chapter.

CHAPTER 2

The k-calculus

An astronomical observation yields an important property of the propagation of light. A spectral analysis of the light of many apparently single stars shows two distinct sets of spectral lines, each executing periodic motions in opposition, so that if one set shifts towards the red, the other shifts towards the violet, and *vice versa*. The only reasonable explanation of such shifts of spectral lines is a velocity with a component along the line of sight. If the source approaches, the frequency of the light received is raised and a violet shift results, and conversely if the source recedes, a red shift is produced. Thus the motion of the spectral lines is accounted for if the optically single star consists in fact of two stars orbiting round each other under the influence of each other's gravitational force. If the plane of the orbit is not too far from the line of sight the phenomenon observed will result, provided only that the light from the advancing and the receding stars arrives together. In other words, the observation shows that there is no overtaking of light by light, irrespective of the speed of the source. Thus the travel of light is wholly unlike the travel of bullets, where the speed of the gun is added to the muzzle velocity. Moreover, the same proportional shift is seen in every part of the spectrum so that in its journey through space the different colours travel at the same speed. Equally the observation of double stars of widely different brightness shows that always in empty space *there is no overtaking of light by light*. Therefore light is so useful as a standard and Milne's radar method of measuring distances is so valuable, in theory and in practice. Thus the speed of light is defined to equal one. On this basis what is called "measuring the speed of light" is in fact a measurement of the unit of length (the Paris meter) in terms of light time. Since a rigid ruler is, from the point of view of physics, a highly complex arrangement of atoms described by the branch known as solid state physics, it is a gain in theoretical simplicity to use only a clock (needed anyway to specify times) and radar, instead of a clock and a ruler.

We now proceed to apply the principle of relativity to a number of ideal experiments involving several inertial observers each.

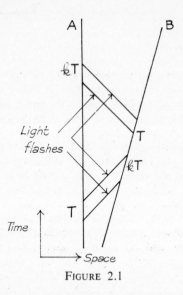

FIGURE 2.1

Since in the main we can confine our attention to inertial observers moving along a single straight line only, we need only use one dimension of space, and can display the motion of our observers readily on a space-time diagram (*Figure 2.1*) in which the vertical represents time and the horizontal co-ordinate the single relevant space dimension. It will be appreciated that an observer at rest in our system of co-ordinates will be represented by a vertical straight line, an observer in motion by an inclined straight line (the greater the angle between the "world line" of the observer and the vertical, the greater is his speed), while an accelerated object will show up as a curve.

Consider now two inertial observers in relative (and of course uniform) motion along a single straight line. We imagine each of them to be equipped with a torch (for signalling) and a clock. In order to avoid any ambiguity about time due to the travelling time of light, each observer always uses his *own clock* in order to record the time of occurrences at his *own* location. One of the observers (to be called A) flashes his torch twice, the interval between the two transmissions as measured by him being time T. The two flashes of light travel towards the other observer (B), who records the time of arrival of the two flashes of light by his own clock. We cannot expect the interval of arrival to be T, since owing to the relative motion of A and B the distance between them (and therefore the time taken by light to cover it) was different when the first flash accomplished the journey and when the second one did so. On the other hand we can be sure that the first flash arrived before the second one, since there is no overtaking of light by light, and the constancy of the relative velocity implies that the interval of reception is proportional to the interval of transmission. Hence we call the interval of reception kT, where k is a real positive number characterising (in a way to be explored later) the velocity of B relative to A. This quantity k will be fundamental to our investigations.

We now reverse the arrangement, asking B to flash his torch twice, at interval T as measured by him, and ask what interval A records between the reception of the two flashes. By a crucial application of the principle of relativity we find that this must again be kT, for if it were in any way different, then A and B would not be *equivalent*. Only complete reciprocity can ensure this equivalence; any discrepancy in the two k values could be interpreted as A being "really" more nearly at rest than B or *vice versa*. Only if it is completely irrelevant which of the two does the transmitting, with the other doing the receiving, can the two observers be considered equivalent as is demanded by the principle of relativity.

We now ask our observers to establish their relative velocity in terms of k. We ask them both to set their clocks to zero when they shoot past each other, and also to exchange light signals at this moment when their distance apart, and therefore the time taken by light to cover it, is negligibly small (*Figure 2.2*). When A's clock shows time T after they pass each other he sends out a second light signal which is then received by B at B's time kT, since transmission and reception of the first signal occurred both at time 0. B immediately sends out an answering light signal, that is an interval kT after B's first signal, which is thus received by A at his time $k(kT) = k^2T$. Thus A's notes on this experiment read:

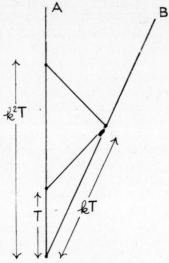

FIGURE 2.2

Time *0:* Sent out light signal to B and received his answer immediately.

Time *T:* Sent out further light signal to B.

Time k^2T: Received B's reply.

Accordingly A will deduce that at the time of B's first response he was at distance zero away from him and at the time of his second response at distance $\frac{1}{2}(k^2 - 1)T$, since the light took time $k^2T - T = (k^2 - 1)T$ to get from him to B and back. Further, A assigns the time $\frac{1}{2}(k^2 + 1)T$ to the moment at which B responds. For light travels at unit velocity, which means that it takes as long to get from A to B at the moment of responding as it takes to get back. Note that this is the time *assigned* by A to a distant event (B's response) and is not a local measurement of time. Note also this is the only reasonable assignment that A can make, for if he attempted to make any allowance for B's velocity then he would have to assign different times to B's response and to the response of another observer moving with different speed but answering from the same place at the same time, which would clearly be highly inconvenient, not to say absurd.

Thus the upshot of A's calculations is that B covered distance $\frac{1}{2}(k^2 - 1)T$ in time $\frac{1}{2}(k^2 + 1)T$, so that he finds for v, the speed of B relative to himself, the value

$$v = \frac{k^2 - 1}{k^2 + 1} \qquad (1)$$

Evidently and necessarily this is also the speed of A relative to B. In equation (1) v turns up as a pure number, which is an obvious consequence of our having chosen the speed of light as standard, so that any other velocity is evaluated as proportion of the speed of light. Next it is seen that $v = 0$ if and only it $k = 1$ (relative rest), that $v > 0$ (recession) if $k > 1$ and $v < 0$ (approach) if $k < 1$. (The validity of (1) for this case is readily established by a minor modification of our argument.) However large k may be, v will not exceed one, and however small k may be, v will never be below — 1. This means that the object measured cannot move faster than light, which is an obvious consequence of our method of measurement, since the light signals could not catch it if it were faster than light.

Solving (1) for k we have

$$k = \sqrt{\frac{1 + v}{1 - v}} \qquad (2)$$

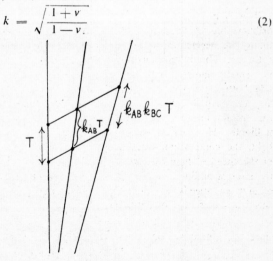

FIGURE 2.3

It is immediately obvious from (2) that changing the sign of v turns k into its reciprocal, a result that will be useful further.

We now consider three inertial observers, A, B, C, all in line with B between A and C, so that they can all be represented on the same space-time diagram (*Figure 2.3*). The k factor between A and B will be denoted by k_{AB}, that between B and C by k_{BC}. What is the value of k_{AC}, the k factor between A and C? If A sends out light signals at interval T, they will be seen by B at interval $k_{AB}T$. If B sends out signals at the moment that he receives A's signals they will be received by A at an interval k_{BC} times the interval of transmission, i.e., at $k_{BC}k_{AB}T$. But since there is no overtaking of light by light, A's signals must arrive at C at the same instant as B's signals and hence with the same interval, which therefore equals $k_{AC}T$. Thus we have the simple law of composition of k factors

$$k_{AC} = k_{AB}\, k_{BC}$$

If each k is expressed in terms of the corresponding v, and the resulting equation is solved for v_{AC} we have, with a little algebra

$$v_{AC} = \frac{v_{AB} + v_{BC}}{1 + v_{AB}v_{BC}}$$

This is Einstein's famous law of composition of velocities. In ordinary life we think it sufficient just to add velocities, which is to say we neglect the term $v_{AB}v_{BC}$ in the denominator compared with one. This is fully justified as long as the velocities are small, i.e., small compared with the speed of light. For example, if we take both v_{AB} and v_{BC} to equal the speed of a fast jet airliner then they each equal only 10^{-6} so that the error made by neglecting the second term in the denominator is only a millionth of a millionth. However, if each speed equals 75% of the speed of light, the composition formula gives a relative velocity of 96% of the speed of light instead of the 150% that would result from the straight addition. Indeed it is easily seen that the composition of any two speeds less than that of light must always lead to a speed less than that of light, for

$$-(1+v_{AB}v_{BC}) < v_{AB}+v_{BC} < 1+v_{AB}v_{BC} \text{ if } -1<v_{AB}<1,\ -1<v_{BC}<1$$

since by subtracting the middle expression we obtain

$$-(1+v_{AB})\,(1+v_{BC})<0\ <(1-v_{AB})\,(1-v_{BC})$$

which is clearly always true.

Also if one of v_{AB}, v_{BC} equals the speed of light, then by (4) v_{AC} equals the speed of light.

Thus the speed of light is a barrier dividing all possible kinds of entities into three classes, (a) slower than light, (b) as fast as light, (c) faster than light, with no possible interchange between any of these classes. Many things are known that fall into class (a), namely all bodies and particles with non-zero mass, such as electrons, protons, etc. In class (b) we know of light and of massless particles such as photons and neutrions. So far the physicists have not come across anything in class (c), and this makes their lives rather easier since any such entity would have very awkward properties.

We are now ready to consider two examples that show up clearly the nature of time in relativity. Time, like any other physical quantity, is defined by the method of measuring it. Thus it is simple elementary caution that has made us ask A to use his own clock to measure his own time, and B to use his own clock to measure his own time. This may have appeared as a harmless, if rather pedantic precaution, since daily experience seems to show it to be unnecessary, with B's time invariably agreeing with A's. However, it must be realized that in our daily experience, and in our "common sense" approach, which is formed by it, the velocities involved are always very small compared with the speed of light. When we consider really high velocities, we move out of the realm of ordinary experience, and the whole purpose and aim of relativity is to deal with problems of high velocities. We have seen in our composition theorem (4) that our ordinary experience, owing to its restricted nature, has failed to present correctly the full denominator which we only obtained from the relativistic approach.

We will now demonstrate more explicitly than is already evident from our derivation of (1) that A's time and B's time do not merge into a single universal public time, as our ordinary experience seems to suggest, but that A, B, and all other inertial observers have their own private times, measured by their own clocks, none preferable to any other, equally good, but not agreeing with each other. Suppose that inertial observer A regards a distant event E to be simultaneous with a local event O. He will do so (*Figure 2.4*) if equal times T have elapsed between the moment P (at which he

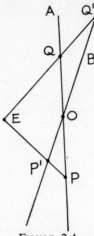

FIGURE 2.4

had to send out a light signal to illuminate E) and 0, and between
0 and the moment Q at which light from E is received by him.
For since the speed of light is unity in each direction he will judge
E to have taken place half-way between P and Q, that is at the
same moment as 0. Consider now another inertial observer, B,
moving so that he passes A at instant 0, being nearer E than A
before 0, and further after 0. If then the k-factor between A and
B has value k after 0 (velocity of separation) it will have had
value $1/k$ before 0 (equal velocity of approach) (see equation (2)).
Thus the moment P' at which B will have had to send out a light
signal to illuminate E will be the moment at which A's signal
passes him, i.e., at time T/k before 0. On the other hand he will
receive the light from E only after it has passed A, at an instant
Q' or time kT after 0. Accordingly in B's judgement, E took place
at a time half-way between P' and Q', that is at time

$$\tfrac{1}{2}(k - \frac{1}{k})T$$

later than 0. In other words, while to A, events 0 and E appear
to be simultaneous, to B it appears that 0 precedes E. To an
observer moving in the opposite direction, E would have appeared

to precede 0. Thus we see that the simultaneity of spatially separated events is purely relative. Two events that to one observer appear to be simultaneous, seem to another to occur in one order, to a third one in the opposite order. Thus the concept of an absolute universal time is clearly incompatible with the principle of relativity.

An even more dramatic example of the relativity of time measurement is the so-called clock paradox, which will be discussed in the next chapter.

CHAPTER 3

Time Stretching

So far the unexpected properties of time that we have discussed have involved only the comparison of times at different places, but it is most instructive to consider a case in which two clocks do not agree on the interval between two events, although both clocks are at the events themselves at the moments of their occurrence. Clearly the clocks must have different experiences between the two events, otherwise they would be together with their readings necessarily coinciding all the way. If, then, one clock travels in an inertial way from one event to the other, the other clock must accomplish the journey in a non-inertial way, since there is only one inertial path (straight line in our diagrams) between any two events.

For our first consideration, instead of employing one non-inertial clock for the alternative path, we may use two differently moving

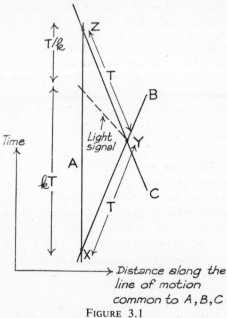

FIGURE 3.1

Timings for three inertial observers, A, B, C.

125

inertial ones in succession. In this arrangement (*Figure 3.1*) we have then three inertial observers A, B, C, all moving in line. Observers B and C have the same speed relative to A, but in opposite directions, and the timing is such that first A and B pass each other (at event X), then B and C (at event Y) and finally C and A (at event Z). The clock of observer B, who is present at both X and Y, measures interval T between these two events. By symmetry, the clock of observer C will measure the equal interval T between events Y and Z at both of which he is present. If then B sets his clock to zero at X, and C sets his clock by B's, when he passes him at Y, then C's clock will read 2T at Z. Supposing A also sets his clock to read zero at X, what will it read at Z? If B sends out light signals to A at X (received immediately) and at Y, then these will be received by A at his times 0 and kT respectively, k being the k-factor between A and B. By an analysis of Equation (2) the k-factor between A and C will be $1/k$, since C's velocity relative to A is the same as B's, but in the opposite direction. Thus if C sends light signals to A at Y and Z, the interval of reception will be T/k. The first one will travel in company with B's (no overtaking of light by light), and will thus reach A when A's clock reads kT, and so the second one will arrive when A's clock reads $kT + T/k$. But since at Z observers C and A coincide, this signal will in fact reach A at Z. Thus we have two measurements for the interval between X and Z:

A's measurement: $(k + \dfrac{1}{k})T$

B's and C's combined measurement: $2T$

Note that, except in the trivial case $k = 1$ (no relative motions at all) A's measurement exceeds that of B and C. Which of them is right? Of course both are right, one giving the time interval *XZ* as measured by an inertial observer present at both, the other as measured by two inertial observers in relative motion. The situation is completely analogous to road distance in a plane which does not depend only on the starting and finishing points of the journey, but also on the *route* taken. In other words, time is a *route dependent* quantity.

If we want to replace the *two* clocks belonging to B and C by just one clock then this must follow a non-inertial, that is, accelerated, track. How does a clock respond to acceleration? This depends on the construction of the clock. A shock-proof watch will work when subjected to acceleration that would destroy an ordinary watch, a time-keeping device consisting of a rabbit hutch in which rabbit generations are being counted would fail if subjected to accelerations that would make the rabbits die (a few g sustained for a little while), a clock consisting of a block of radium (whose mass was being measured to determine the fraction decayed into radon gas) could stand very high acceleration indeed, and so on. Each type of clock has a limiting acceleration. If this is not exceeded, the clock will work. If therefore B has a tough clock which he throws to C at Y, C catching it neatly, then this clock will register $2T$ at Z, just like the combined measurement of B and C. This clock will indicate a shorter time than A's clock, because it has suffered accelerations, just as a road is longer than the direct one because it has curves. Note that both accelerations and curves are *absolute* in the sense that they can be found by local observation without reference to any outside object. If one is being driven along a curvy road, one knows about it without looking at the bends in the road.

Note that a curved road is longer than a straight one *because* it has curves, without the extra length having to lie *in* the curves (*Figure 3.2*). Two straight sections joined by a short, sharp bend can make a road far longer than the direct straight line between the start and the finish, with the curve itself containing hardly any of the extra length. "Straight almost all the way" is totally different in its effect on distance from "straight all the way". Similarly the clock thrown from B to C moving inertially almost all the time (*i.e.*, except while being thrown and caught) registers quite a

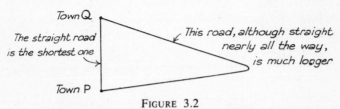

FIGURE 3.2
Map showing two towns and the roads joining them.

different time from A's clock which is always inertial. There is thus no reciprocity between the two clocks; the experience of the one will be wholly different from the experience of the other. If each is placed into a bag of raw eggs at the start of the experiment, the clock thrown from B to C will arrive in an awful mess, while A's clock will be quite clean.

The experimental tests of this route-dependent behaviour of time are closely related to another experimental test of relativity, namely, the increase of mass with velocity. To derive this, we return to the experiment used to establish *Equation (1)* linking k-factor and velocity. It will be recollected that B's clock measured time kT as having elapsed between his passing A and receiving A's second light signal, while A assigned the interval

$$\tfrac{1}{2}(k^2 + 1)T$$

to this period. In other words, when A assigns intervals of time to happenings at B, making the best allowance he can for the travel time of light, he obtains values greater than B's own measurements of these intervals by the factor

$$\frac{k^2 + 1}{2k} = \tfrac{1}{2}\left(k + \frac{1}{k}\right) = (1 - v^2)^{-\frac{1}{2}} \tag{5}$$

the last expression arising from substituting (2) into either of the other expressions. In other words, A finds that things happen more slowly at B than B himself does.

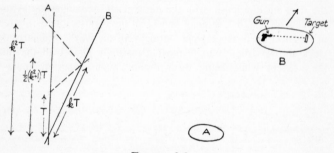

FIGURE 3.3

Space-time diagram (left) and pictorial representation (right) of experiment in which B moves directly away from A and fires bullets at right angles to his velocity relative to A, at a target, to measure their penetrating power.

Let us now suppose that A and B measure distances at right angles to their relative motion, that is, at right angles to the paper in our representation (*Figure 3.3*). It is immediately plausible and can indeed be proved (though the proof is a little lengthy and will not be given here) that A and B agree on these distances. Imagine now that A and B are space travellers and that B shoots various bullets from various guns in the direction at right angles to the relative motion of A and B at a variety of pieces of armour platings held across the path of the bullets. We shall also suppose that whether or not a bullet penetrates armour of given thickness depends only on its normal momentum, that is, the product of its mass and the component of its velocity at right angles to the force of the armour plating. Incidentally, we shall suppose the velocity of the bullets as measured by B to be quite small compared with the relative velocity of A and B. Observer A is watching these experiments and clearly he will agree with B on whether a bullet penetrates the armour plating or not, and on how thick the armour plating is and how far the gun is from it, for these distances are at right angles to the relative velocity of A and B. Accordingly, A and B agree on the penetrating power and hence on the normal momentum of the bullets but they disagree on their velocity, since in A's measurement the interval between the moment when a bullet leaves the gun and when it hits the armour is greater than in B's view, by the factor (5). Hence A will deduce a mass for B's bullets greater than B himself does by just the factor (5). In other words, A regards the mass of B's bullets to be *enhanced* by B's speed relative to A. Thus we have deduced an increase of mass with velocity. This is very accurately susceptible to measurement in the great particle accelerators used to smash atomic nuclei. The test so performed is perhaps the most sensitive and precise of the many tests of special relativity, in all of which experiment and theory are in excellent agreement.*

---

*Historically, relativity was based on the celebrated experiment of Michelson and Morley in which it was found that the motion of the earth had no effect on the speed of light. In the modern view, in which the speed of light equals one by definition, such a test is pointless, and even as a measurement of the effect of the Earth's motion on the length of measuring rods is of little significance since the interatomic forces determining the length of a rod are electromagnetic and much like radar in fixing interatomic distances, but of course the whole modern view was shaped by the Michelson-Morley experiment.

To interpret this increase of mass with velocity we recollect that
for small v

$$(1 - v^2)^{-\frac{1}{2}} = 1 + \tfrac{1}{2}v^2 + \ldots$$

so that the extra mass found by A for a body whose mass B regards
as m is, for small v,

$$\tfrac{1}{2}mv^2$$

This is the familiar Newtonian expression for kinetic energy
(valid of course only for small v, since Newtonian theory does not
apply for v comparable with one, the speed of light). Thus we can
say that kinetic energy has mass and, since the most characteristic
property of all forms of energy is its interchangeability, we are
driven to conclude that all energy has mass. Indeed, many tests
confirm the correctness of this conclusion. In our units the extra
mass just equals the energy, but in conventional units this is
different. We first note that we must write w/c where we wrote v,
where w is the velocity in any units and c the velocity of light in
the same units, since our v is the ratio of the speed of the body
to the speed of light. Thus the extra mass M of energy E is given
by

$$M - \frac{E}{c^2}$$

a famous result of Einstein's. In ordinary units this means that the
large energy of 25 million kWh (costing, at $1\frac{1}{2}$ pence a unit, over
£150,000) has a mass of only 1 gram.

Consider now the speeding up of a fast particle, as occurs for
example in a particle accelerator. As we have seen, we cannot
increase its velocity to the speed of light or beyond, but we can
speed it up from 90% of the speed of light to 99% then to 99.9%,
then to 99.99% and so on. The actual change of speed in the
later stages is thus not very large. However, by (5), each such
successive step will lead to a substantial increase in mass,
momentum, energy, and time stretching, each of these being
controlled by (5), thus increasing the speed from 99% of the speed
of light to 99.99% increases each of these by a factor close on 10,
and a virtually equal factor results in going from 99.99% to
99.9999%, although the actual speed of the particles is only
increased by 30 km/sec. Similar factors of about 10 result whenever

we divide the difference between the speed of the particle and that of light by 100. Thus speeding up an already very fast particle makes it go hardly any faster, but it increases substantially its energy and therefore its mass, its momentum and thus its penetrating power. In the sense discussed earlier, it makes the observer relative to whom the speed is measured see developments on the particle enormously slowed down. This last fact is readily observable. Some of the particles produced in an accelerator are unstable and decay into other particles. Evidently the time of such decay is controlled by the structure of the particle and is thus time as measured by an observer travelling with the particle. The distance the physicist observes the particle to travel between production and decay is the product of its speed and the decay time, as measured by the physicist. Two particles of the same kind, one going at 99.99% of the speed of light, the other at 99.9999% should therefore have decay paths effectively 10 times as long for the second particle as for the first, not directly because it is going faster, but because by (5) the physicist sees its "clock" (i.e. its decay mechanism) operate 10 times more slowly. This effect is easily and frequently observed and is thus another important test of relativity and particularly of the reality of time stretching.

CHAPTER 4

Time and Gravitation

The most important property of gravitation, discovered by Galileo, is that all bodies fall equally fast. This property sets gravitation totally apart from all other forces.

In Newton's second law of dynamics, *force* is put equal to *mass times acceleration*. The full significance of this law is not always appreciated. In the first instance it shows (like the first law) that *acceleration* is what has to be accounted for by a force, not *velocity*. Secondly, it shows that different bodies respond with different accelerations when subjected to the same force. (The typical experiment here is a spring, always compressed to the same length, successively shoving different bodies along a smooth horizontal plane.) The power of resistance of a body to being accelerated is called its *inertia* and is measured by its *inertial mass,* which is the mass quantity entering Newton's second law. The force quantity is supposed to be one of a list of available forces and it is implicitly assumed that it is indeed feasible, as in our spring example above, for the *same* force to act successively on different bodies. Often the specification of the force includes the property of the body to which the force hooks on, as it were. For example, if the force is an electric one, then its magnitude is proportional to the *electric charge* the body carries. If this is doubled, the force is doubled; if it is reduced to zero, the force is reduced to zero. If we have two bodies, of different masses, but carrying the same charge, the same force will pull the bodies, though of course they will move with different accelerations. (We have assumed here that the same body can carry various and different charges. This is correct for an ordinary size body, but *e.g.,* all electrons carry the same charge.)

The gravitational field, like the electric field, hooks on to a particular property of a body, and this property is called its *passive gravitational mass*. When the gravitational field is the earth's surface field, we call the force exerted on a body its *weight,* which is thus the product of the local field and the body's passive gravitational mass. When we weigh a body on a spring balance we ascertain its passive gravitational mass by measuring the force exerted on it by the earth through seeing how far a spring has to extend before it can exactly counter the pull of gravitation.

Galileo's result that all bodies fall equally fast implies that they all show the same acceleration. Hence the forces exerting on different bodies must be proportional to their inertial masses and thus we can restate the result in the form: **The ratio of passive gravitational mass to inertial mass is the same for all bodies.**

This law has been tested to a high degree of accuracy. The classical method of testing it is to consider that at a point on the surface of the earth a body not only suffers the gravitational attraction of the earth but also centrifugal (*i.e.,* inertial) force due to the earth's rotation. These two forces are in general not in the same direction. Thus if the two forces did not act on two bodies in the same ratio, the combined force (which is what we normally appreciate as effective gravity) would not act in exactly the same direction on the two bodies. Eotyös found early in this century from an experiment devised to measure such a difference of direction, that for the wide variety of materials tested, the ratio of the two masses could not differ by more than at most one part in 10^7 and modern work by Dicke has improved this to one part in 10^9. Thus Galileo's result holds with very great accuracy.

It should be mentioned in passing that there exists a third definition of mass, *active gravitational mass*. This measures the ability of a body to produce a gravitational field. If we determine the mass of the earth by measuring its attraction on the moon, then we are evaluating its power as the source of gravitation and thus we measure its active gravitational mass, which is indeed the mass normally determined in astronomy, *e.g.,* by measuring the attraction the sun exerts on the planets, or the two components of a double star exert on each other. Newton's third law of dynamics on the equality of action and reaction demands that active and passive gravitational masses should be proportional to each other. Thus we have three definitions of mass (inertial, active and passive gravitational) according to three different means of measuring mass. If we accept that all bodies fall equally fast and that action equals reaction, then the ratio of the three is the same for all bodies and, in suitable units, they are all equal to each other. Thus the general term *mass* is justified but, as we may always have new theories in which the old laws hold only approximately and not precisely, it is desirable to keep the distinctions between the different kinds of mass in mind.

An important relation between gravitation and time can be derived by putting together a number of ideas some of which have already been discussed:

(i) Energy has mass (see the previous Chapter).

(ii) Inertial and passive gravitational mass are the same and are just mass.

(iii) We cannot have an engine that constantly produces energy without producing any other changes. In technical language this important principle is called the impossibility of a *perpetuum mobile,* in colloquial language it is expressed as "You cannot get money for jam".

(iv) Radiation is emitted and absorbed by atoms only in quanta, packets of energy proportional to the frequency of the radiation. This is the very foundation of quantum theory, and was discovered by Max Planck in 1900. The emission of radiation changes an atom from a state of higher energy to a state of lower energy, and the reverse process occurs during the absorption of radiation.

(v) The frequency emitted by any type of atom or molecule in a specified line of its spectrum can serve as standard of time. It is indeed used in this way in the caesium and ammonia clocks that form the basis for the world's time standards. The forces responsible for defining such frequencies are of the same kind as the forces that give a hairspring its strength and so determine the rate of a watch, but the operation of a pendulum clock is quite different.

We can now devise an experiment which, while it cannot be carried out with present technology, can yet be defined and thoroughly discussed theoretically.

We imagine a high tower on the earth, and an endless chain of buckets running over pulleys at the foot and at the top of the tower (*Figure 4.1*). We now load all the buckets on one side of the chain with atoms of a particular species in a state of low energy, and all the buckets on the other side with the same number of atoms of the same species but in a state of higher energy. By (i)

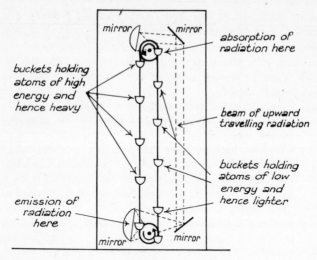

FIGURE 4.1
Bucket and chain construction of "perpetuum mobile".

the side with the more energetic atoms will have more mass and by (ii) this means that it will be heavier and so this side will begin to move downwards. We now arrange that these energetic atoms emit radiation by (iv) as they pass the lower pulley, thereby going into the state of low energy. We catch the radiation in mirrors, direct it as a beam to the top of the tower and focus it on the low energy atoms as they pass over the top pulley, so that they absorb the energy and pass over into the more energetic state. The system is now in a steady state, with the whole chain in motion and one side of it always heavier than the other. We can therefore keep on abstracting energy from the pulleys (*e.g.*, by making them drive electric generators) without anything else changing, contrary to (iii). Accordingly there must be a fault in our argument. But all the steps can basically take place except perhaps for one single point: we have assumed that when the radiation is focused on the atoms at the top pulley, its frequency and thus its quanta are just right to be absorbed and to change the atoms from the lower to the higher state of energy. Hence this assumption must be wrong. Radiation

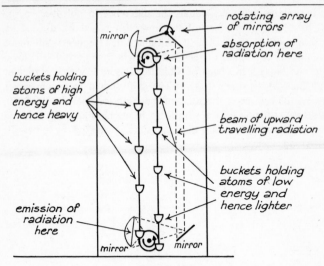

rotating array of mirrors

absorption of radiation here

mirror

buckets holding atoms of high energy and hence heavy

beam of upward travelling radiation

buckets holding atoms of low energy and hence lighter

emission of radiation here

mirror   mirror

FIGURE 4.2

Bucket and chain experiment, with rotating mirrors.

locally emitted by atoms changing from the higher to the lower state can be absorbed to change them back, but radiation so emitted low down cannot. Since we are suffering from a surplus of energy we must assume that the quanta have too little energy, *i.e.,* too low a frequency. We can check that this is so by using a moving mirror to raise the frequency. By the Doppler shift *(Chapter 2)* when radiation is reflected by an approaching mirror, time intervals are reduced and so the frequency is raised. However, it requires energy to do this since the radiation exerts a pressure on the mirror, so that it needs energy to move the mirror against the radiation. Using mirrors on a rotating axis we can now restore the steady state of the system *(Figure 4.2)*, but while there is a power output from the pulleys of the chain there has also to be a power input into the spindle of the mirror system. If this input were less than the output, there would still be a net gain of energy, contrary to (iii); if it were more, we could run the system in reverse and still draw out energy, and so the mirrors must require just as much energy as the chain yields. This consideration allows us to calculate the frequency deficiency Δv of the radiation (of frequency v). It emerges that $\Delta v/v$ equals the difference in potential energy (gh) between top and foot of the tower (of height h), divided by the square of the speed of light. Although this frequency difference is minute for any tower of reasonable height (one part in 10^{15} for a tower 40′ high) it has been possible to measure it with a particular γ-ray line (Mösshauer effect).* The shift should be much longer between the surface of the sun and the earth (one part in 500,000), but atoms radiating on the sun do so in circumstances so different from laboratory situations that the shift is masked by other ill-understood ones.

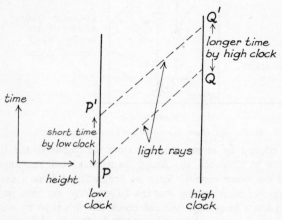

FIGURE 4.3

Gravitational time stretching implies that although PQQ′p′ is a parallelogram, the time PP′ differs from the time QQ′, both being measured with local clocks of identical construction.

Why is the frequency received on top of the tower low? An often advanced argument says that the quanta emitted at the foot have energy and therefore mass. Energy is required to lift a mass against gravity and this energy can only be abstracted from the quanta themselves. Diminishing their energy is the same as diminishing their frequency, with the result as given. On the other hand this argument, in spite of its plausibility, is seriously misleading. We cannot, after all, envisage the electromagnetic waves

*This is the celebrated experiment of Pound and Rebka.

making up the radiation actually to lose cycles on the way. How absurd this would be, becomes clear when we imagine the vibrations controlling clocks. In a static gravitational field one cannot see from the top a clock at the bottom losing more and more time *unless it actually does so.* In other words, the only tenable interpretation of the gravitational shift of spectral lines is as follows: Suppose we have, side by side, two clocks of identical construction and rate. If we now lower one of them in our gravitational field, then in the lower position, as a result of having been moved through the field, it will advance at a slower rate than the other clock which remains in its original position. This slowing down of clocks is a fundamental feature of the gravitational field, inescapable on the basis of our physical principles (i) to (v).

If we use clocks and light-rays to measure out the world, this shift has a most important consequence: Consider in a space-time diagram (*Figure 4.3*) the quadrilateral made up of the two clocks, top and bottom, and two light-rays joining them. Since the situation is static, the two light-rays must be parallel to each other, and the lines representing the clocks are also parallel to each other, so that the quadrilateral is a parallelogram. But the two clocks will measure different lengths of time between the rays because of the gravitational shift. Thus opposite sides of the parallelogram are not of equal length, showing we require a *non-Euclidean geometry* to depict the gravitational field. Our best theory of gravitation, general relativity, is indeed based on such a geometry. It is fully relativistic in the sense that special relativity, as discussed in *Chapters 1-3,* holds everywhere locally, and it gives correctly the gravitational red shift as derived above. Unfortunately, the non-Euclidean geometry makes its mathematics rather heavy.

THE ARROW OF TIME

by

T. Gold

T. GOLD
*Professor of Astronomy and Director of the
Cornell University Center for Radiophysics and
Space Research, Cornell University, Ithaca, N.Y.*

The Arrow of Time

Much of our understanding of the world is based on the particular sense organs we have. Our preoccupation with geometry, the geometrical configurations of all things around us, is no doubt due to the excellence of the eye for acquiring such information. The idea of expressing basic laws of physics in terms of forces no doubt arose because our muscles are equipped with sense organs that signal the force applied. These may all be perfectly sensible ways of analysing the outside world; but they may be not as unique as we are tempted to think. There may be other ways—that we cannot now conceive—that are as good or even better for obtaining an understanding of the physical world around us.

This, I think, is the situation with time. We all have, as the most basic proof of our consciousness, the sensation of the passing of time. Just as we cannot conceive describing the outside world without reference to its geometrical properties, so we cannot describe it without reference to the passage of time.

Yet is that really the only way of describing the world? Is there really a uniform flow of time within which events occur?

We are familiar with describing an event in terms of the three co-ordinates of three-dimensional space—*where* it occurred—and one co-ordinate of time—*when* it occurred. An object may in this framework occupy any region of the space co-ordinates, or continue to remain in one place; but it cannot fail to slide along the time co-ordinate. Who is pushing it? Why can it not stand still? Why does it move in the one direction and not in the other along the time axis? These questions may be silly; there may be no answer to *"why?"* questions, if that is how the world is constructed. Explanations in physics can explain any particular thing only in terms of something more general. A particular occurrence, can be explained in terms of laws of physics, the most general descriptions we have found. But how could we ever "explain" the broadest generalizations? Time flows—that is a law of physics; that is how the universe operates.

It is difficult, however, to leave the question there, to be satisfied with such a statement, if one knows certain things about the physical world. Perhaps the flowing of time is only a description of a subjective impression. Perhaps our minds create the illusion, and force us to describe the exterior world in these terms. Perhaps there is no feature of the exterior world that demands such a flow of time, but the need to describe it in terms that fit our consciousness, forces us towards it.

Let us try to understand the position of time in the framework of the laws of physics. It is used there as a co-ordinate, and any interval along the direction of this co-ordinate can be measured by an instrument called a clock. If we did not have clocks we could use certain types of physical processes that are known to run at a constant rate—the falling of sand through an orifice, the swing of a pendulum, a weight oscillating on a spring, etc. These processes are known to run at a standard rate in the sense that one can keep comparing them against each other and the results do not change. They give the impression, therefore, of an even flow of time underlying all processes we see. "Mathematical time", as Newton called it, is the ideal, and actual clocks differ in their indications from it through their individual imperfections. It is implied that there is only one "mathematical time", and therefore that "perfect clocks", whatever their principle of operation, will all go alike. What does that mean? What definition can we give of two clocks going alike? Obviously not that they tick at the same frequency, since I can arbitrarily adjust the rate of ticking of a pendulum or a weight-and-spring. But what is assumed to be constant is the *ratio* of the number of ticks made in any given interval. A given pendulum and a weight-and-spring may have any ratio of their frequencies but, it is assumed, if nothing changes in their construction they will always have that same ratio. It is just as with a measuring stick that is assumed to be of constant length, though not necessarily the same as another. But, if no changes take place in their construction, it is assumed that they both will measure in the same ratio, no matter whether the object being measured is in Sydney, New York or on the moon.

It is, of course, an assumption that there is a "mathematical time" as Newton clearly realized, and that there is only one type. Milne realized this and challenged the assumption by looking into the consequences of having two different ones, depending on the physical principle employed. If gravitation is the force involved in making the oscillation then one type of time would be measured; if atomic forces were involved, then it would be the other. We shall not discuss this possibility further here.

The assumption of one "mathematical time" can be expressed as the assumption of the homogeneity of space-time. *Homogeneous* means *uniform* in position; any place is like any other. If the laws of physics make a weight-and-spring beat in a certain ratio with another periodic device at one location of space-time, they do so at another. The laws of physics operate in a homogeneous space-time. This could all be described on a space-time diagram in which we fix the units along the time co-ordinate by means of one clock, and along the space co-ordinates by means of measuring rods, and where we would then find another clock described in the diagram marking off even intervals along the time co-ordinate, wherever it was placed (but, as you know, only so long as it is in uniform motion).

Does this tell us anything about the flow of time? We would really like to know why time progresses at all, and I have not discussed any more than that it progresses at the same rate at different places and different times. That has not got us any further yet. Any feature of the entire physical world can be described on space-time diagrams, as the world lines of all the particles of matter. Even if we could not make a diagram comprehensive enough to depict the entire universe, past, present and future, we can still contemplate having a sample of a representative locality. Suppose we had a very substantial piece of this diagram in front of us. Would we see in it any reason for the apparent "flow" of time?

The physical laws would all be represented in this comprehensive diagram as certain regularities in the pattern. The discovery of laws of nature is, after all, nothing other than the recognition of certain regularities in the great pattern of world lines. The fact that we think of ourselves as drifting along the direction of the time co-ordinate through this pattern was in no way essential to the discovery of these regularities—had we seen the entire pattern at once we could have spotted them at least as well.

But let us be quite clear about this. All of the physical world is contained in this great pattern. Yet in it, there is nothing that suggests any intrinsic division into past and future, and an edge representing the present, sliding relentlessly along. In fact, as you know from the Special Relativity which Professor Bondi has been explaining to you, there would not even be the possibility of such an edge representing the present, being defined in a consistent way so that it could be meaningful for observers no matter in what state of motion they were. This sliding edge has a meaning for each one of us, but it clearly is wrong to think of it as existing in an absolute way in our great pattern. In other words, the physical world as a whole is not divided into past, present and future. We make these concepts and then try to force them into our understanding of nature. Why?

All I can hope for is that at the end of these lectures we will be a little closer to an understanding of the central problem: *Why it is that we live with this firm impression of the passage of time, and how the physical world around us has given us the possibility of forming such an impression.* In the process we will have to understand many more strange things about the nature of the physical world, but, what is more difficult, we will have to unlearn things that have become apparently self evident. "It ain't what a man does not know that makes him a fool; it is what he does know that ain't so!" That is the famous saying of a comedian who would have made a good physicist.

The Sense of a Clock

Let us start with clocks. We have discussed them already, but really only one aspect of them—the ticking, the marking off of equal time intervals. But that is not all one requires of a clock. Just a pendulum swinging on a wall would not be satisfactory. It has to show the time; and that means not only that an indicating system has to count the ticks—that is trivial—but it has to know in what sense to count them. It has to know which is earlier and which is later. Now, of course, you and I know that without any trouble; why not the clock? It is easy to arrange for a clock to go round the right way. If it went round the wrong way we would just reverse some gears and put it right. There is no technical problem there—but there is one of understanding why all this is so easy.

The clock did not know in which sense it had to go, but *we* did. Our conscious awareness of the passage of time could always be used without fail to calibrate the sense of the indications of the clock. The sense any clock indicates for the progress of time is merely the sense some person knew was right. We still have not found the forward flow of time in the physical world, but only in ourselves.

The Time-symmetry of Nature

But the story is much more mysterious still. Not only is it difficult to find a flow of time represented in simple processes, it seems to be impossible to find it in the very simplest. The basic laws of physics appear to be symmetrical with time; that is to say, they would represent the world just as well if time went the other way. Let us consider some examples of this. The laws of dynamics and gravitation, described first by Newton, make no distinction between the two senses of time. A process completely described by them can therefore occur just as well in reverse. The motion of the planets in the solar system is one such example—if we reversed all motions exactly, the system would still be just as good an example of Newton's laws, but its description would now be identical with that of the real one with the time reversed. The same thing is true in electro-magnetism. The motion, for example, of an electric charge in an electro-magnetic field and a description with the time reversed are both equally good examples of the laws of electro-magnetism. Also, there is no difference in the description of the emission process of light and a description of an absorption process with the time reversed. Quantum theory did not remove this strange symmetry either, nor did the theory of relativity. It seems that in each case the investigators responsible did not have any particular bias in favour of a time symmetrical theory, but it just turned out that way. Each new set of phenomena when it came to be understood and described in the most general terms, turned out to have no sense of time built in.

Just in recent times, this statement has to be qualified a little bit;

because just now there is some discussion whether an elementary process in nuclear physics has been discovered which is not time symmetrical. It is not yet clear what this observation implies and perhaps we shall have to revise our discussion; but we must still regard it as very strange that all the major events in our surroundings are dictated by time symmetrical laws while we have so clearly an idea that time is unsymmetrical.

The Asymmetry of the Real World

Clearly, a lot of the actual things that happen are not time symmetrical. We only have to run a movie backwards to see that. Who could jump out of the water feet first and gracefully land on a high diving board upright? When has it ever happened that sand jumped up spontaneously off a heap and arranged itself neatly on a workman's shovel to be put carefully into a hole? Who has ever seen the fragments of a flower pot jump together on the floor and instantly weld themselves into a perfect piece in a person's hands? We do not have to look at a film for very long to see that it is reversed. Although to be sure, not all scenes would give it away. How is it now: which scenes would give it away, and which not?

Suppose you had a train running around a track. Would you know? You might say that it would be odd for the engine to be at the back, pushing, but not impossible. How about a car? You would say that no driver limited to the human range of skills could manage to drive the thing in reverse at 60 miles an hour and not smash up instantly; but could you prove that it is impossible to make a car that could go in reverse at this speed or find a driver who could master this skill? But then the scene in our movie might shift to a waterfall boiling and foaming at the bottom with the violence of the colliding water masses. Anyone would be sure there; the water is coming from the top and crashing down. No one could devise a way of making a boiling and bubbling mass of water and arrange to have emerge out of it a jet that gracefully coalesces and smoothly slides over the rock ledge a hundred feet above. That is just impossible.

Or there might be a scene of cream being poured into a cup of coffee and being stirred up. Again, no one would think it possible to have the coffee stirred in such an artfully contrived manner that all the cream droplets would coagulate together and form a single block.

Or suppose there is a scene of an airplane taking off. Could that be a landing in reverse? Could a plane fly backwards? Of course not.

So the interesting fact emerges that there are some types of events that are strongly directional in time and there are those that are less so or not so at all. The closer we go to the simplest, most elementary processes, the most non-directional, on the whole, things get. When we decomposed any kind of event into the elementary processes, then we lost the directionality that was clearly implied in the event as a whole. If we looked in detail at the molecules of water jostling each other in the waterfall's whirlpool, we would see many processes that could all go in reverse just as well. But if we look at larger and larger regions of this whirlpool it becomes less and less likely as a process in the opposite sense of time. If we looked at the flow of air over an airplane's structure on the microscopic scale we would not find any laws of physics infringed by the reverse flow. But again, if we look on the larger scale, the reverse flow would contain more and more events that we would say that are not in detail impossible, but are just extremely unlikely to go that way. Everything would look highly contrived and, while one would have to admit that the motion is a possible one with the detailed conditions of the position and movement of all the molecules involved, one would say that no one could have managed to contrive these initial conditions exactly such that the very unlikely results would follow.

Let us try to understand all this more clearly. Instead of classifying movies as those that do and those that don't have a sense of time, let us look at a simpler situation. Suppose we have a ball on a tray and we take some snapshots of it. We are told that the system was not interfered with during the entire period during which photographs were taken, but that it may have been interfered with before and after that period, and that it may, of course, have been left in a state of motion. If those snapshots are all shuffled, can you put them in the right order?

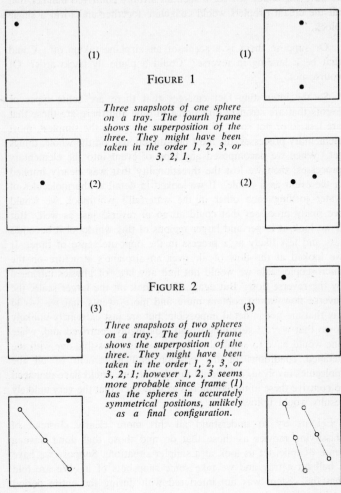

FIGURE 1

Three snapshots of one sphere on a tray. The fourth frame shows the superposition of the three. They might have been taken in the order 1, 2, 3, or 3, 2, 1.

FIGURE 2

Three snapshots of two spheres on a tray. The fourth frame shows the superposition of the three. They might have been taken in the order 1, 2, 3, or 3, 2, 1; however 1, 2, 3 seems more probable since frame (1) has the spheres in accurately symmetrical positions, unlikely as a final configuration.

FIGURE 1   FIGURE 2

The answer is: you can put them in the right *sequence* if they represent sufficiently small time intervals. We can deduce the *sequence* but not the *sense in time*. 1, 2, 3, 4, 5 or 5, 4, 3, 2, 1; we cannot tell which. The laws of motion of the ball are time symmetrical and therefore either sense of its motion is acceptable. If the successive positions are just such that they would fit an undisturbed motion in either sense, then we will, no doubt, presume that this is the explanation and put the pictures in that sequence.

Or suppose that we have the same situation, but with two balls. Again we are told that during the period when the snapshots were taken there was no interference, but before and after there may have been. Again the snapshots can be ordered in a sequence—but now there may be a hint of the correct direction of time of that sequence. What if, for example, the two balls were lying in precise symmetrical places at one end of the sequence? Would we then not suppose that somebody started it out that way? Is it not too unlikely to find a neat arrangement at the end of the period?

With two balls, the probabilities are perhaps not too terribly small against the latter having arisen by chance, so we cannot be quite sure. But what if we had two thousand? Then surely any very systematic pattern would have to be at the beginning of the interval, for how could you think that it would have happened by chance at the end after a lot of random looking arrangements.

This is how we could tell the sense of the sequence if the arrangement in fact had been a favourable one for our purposes

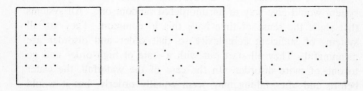

FIGURE 3

Three snapshots of many spheres on a tray. The order 1, 2, 3 now seems very much more probable than any other, since the regular configuration on (1) would be unlikely to be the end product of the motion. (2) is likely to be intermediate, with the motion having not yet led to as random an appearance as (3).

at the beginning. But if it was not, then we still could not tell.
If the configuration at the beginning looks as random as that at the
end, there is no possibility. The strange conclusion then emerges:
with a few balls in the field we cannot be quite sure ever. With a
lot we can be very sure if we happen to have a very particular
situation set up at the beginning. If not, the *sequence* can be
inferred but not the *sense*.

How does all this compare with the situation with the clock
that we discussed before? There we decided that it was a person
who knew the sense, not the clock. Here we have it that we are
prepared to infer that a person had set up the system at the
beginning in some particular way and that the application of the
laws of nature would then take it further away from this particular
condition. Again, the intervention of a person is required for the
sense of time to be inferred. Is that always the rule? Is there
nothing other than people who know which way time runs?

What about the waterfall? Here we have a natural phenomenon
which has a sense built in. Here also a lot of objects are involved—
all the droplets into which the water can break up—and indeed
if we look closely enough, all the molecules. That, as always,
seems to help. But in this case it was not necessary for the initial
condition to be one contrived in some particular way by a person.
With snapshots taken in close succession, we could easily recognize
the paths of many droplets and we would then arrange the sequence
such that the water falls down on the whole and not up. The
sense of flow of the water going upwards is not one that could be
expected even though it is not quite impossible.

What is expected? It is always that an ordered or systematic
system would give way to an unordered random one. All systems
that show the sense of time have this in common. They are all
systems of sufficient complexity so that order and disorder are
meaningful. They all start out with a state of high order and go
to one of more disorder. In the case of the waterfall, the water
before and after falling may seem equally orderly, but it would
not be if we looked in detail, for all that violent disorder at the
bottom, when it gives way to a smooth stream again, will still have
left its effect on the water. Instead of the big droplets rushing
around in a disorderly fashion, it will eventually be the molecules

of the water that will do so individually, since the water is now somewhat warmer. The increased disorder is still there, even if it is harder to see it.

Order and Disorder

What is order and disorder? Can we always define it properly? In some cases the definition seems obvious, as in the case of heating a perfectly regular crystal lattice of a solid material and causing it to melt into an irregular, nearly random, arrangement of its molecules. But I could invent other cases, for example with the spheres on my tray, where a precisely systematic pattern may go unnoticed. What if I set up the spheres to occupy the positions on a co-ordinate grid of precisely the prime numbers? It might not look very systematic if one did not look for this particular effect. If one did, it would suffice just as any other systematic pattern to tell the sense in time of the snapshots. But if one did not recognize the particular regularity, one just could not find the sense of the sequence of snapshots. If we don't have a good definition of order and disorder, then it only means that in all the doubtful cases we might not be able to recognize the sense of time in the system.

We now see clearly why we usually need a complex situation described on our snapshots. The more objects we can see on our snapshots, the easier it will be to recognize order and disorder.

To be able to find a sequence in our snapshots, we required not only the complexity but also that in fact in the beginning there must have been some recognizable order. This could have arisen either from a person having done it, having disposed the objects in some systematic pattern, or from nature having produced somehow an orderly situation in some natural way; either will do. If the system is then allowed to go on for long enough, it will eventually end up in a less orderly configuration and our snapshots will show the effect.

In practice, we often have systems with such vast numbers of particles that order and disorder are extremely meaningful concepts. It is for these circumstances that one has devised a measure of the disorder of a system and has given it the name of *entropy*. In thermo-dynamics one discusses the relation between this entropy specifying the degree of disorder of a system and its content of heat and of energy that could be made available in the system.

Order and disorder, or entropy, assumes a new significance when it becomes possible to define in those terms the available energy of a system. Order and disorder and energy seem very different things, so how do these two come to be connected?

It is quite easy to understand the connection between energy and order-disorder by means of a simple example. Suppose we have a very well heat-insulated box and in it we have two large pieces of copper, one very hot and the other very cold. We know that if we left them in the box for a long time they would eventually assume the same temperature—the hot piece would have cooled itself and the cold piece would have got heated until there no longer was a temperature difference and nothing more would happen after that. The heat energy contained in the box as a whole would not have been changed by that. What is happening there is not very different from the discussion we had about the spheres on the tray. Here again, we have a highly ordered situation at the beginning, namely that nearly all the heat energy is concentrated in the one piece and very little in the other, and if we leave it to itself it will get itself into the more disordered condition in terms of the energy content of the individual molecules. Again, as before, it would not, in principle, be impossible for all the heat energy to concentrate itself back in the one block, but it is now a process which is so exceedingly unlikely that we need not discuss it. If we had only two molecules, then it would not be very unlikely. But since we have a very large number, all statistical probabilities are virtually certainties.

In this case a thermo-dynamicist would speak of the entropy of the system increasing as heat flows from the hot body to the cold body. He would then point out that, at the beginning, it would have been possible to extract energy from the system by placing a heat engine, say a steam engine, to be heated by the hot block so as to have its radiator (where it gets rid of heat) connected to the cold block. The shaft of this engine would then have made available energy that could have been used in any way one likes. If, on the other hand, one lets time elapse and hence entropy increase, then eventually when the two blocks have reached the same temperature, no engine could be made to work using this heat energy. The energy would still be there, of course, but it is now in such a state of disorder that we could no longer see any way of getting hold of it.

In the language of the thermo-dynamicist, entropy in any system appears always to increase. If entropy somewhere is seen to decrease—if for example someone is setting up the hot and the cold blocks by means of, say, a flame and a refrigerator—then one can enquire what the other effects of this equipment are; it will always be seen that, if one encompasses the system as a whole that contains the flame and the refrigerator and its fuel and so forth, that that system as a whole would have suffered an increase of entropy, even though some subsystem had suffered a decrease. It seems that things can only be ordered at the expense of making more disorder somewhere else.

Why did we get into all this for the discussion of time? We wanted to see what it was that characterized those systems in which the sense of time was evident. The hot and the cold blocks in our box are now a very good example, for there we don't need to know too accurately how to specify order and disorder. It is quite clear in which sense things will go. Is it true that all systems that contain a sense of time are of this kind? Is the arrow of time given only by the sense in which disorder increases?

A simple answer to this question is "yes". All the systems that we have discussed and all the others that we might equally have used as examples are of that kind. Even the clock might have been included if we had gone a little further with its discussion. The clock, in addition to ticking away intervals, has in fact a process going on which is not time symmetrical. I am referring to the fact that the mainspring will get unwound and the energy that was stored up there will reappear as heat throughout the mechanism. Energy has gone from an accessible form to one of so much disorder that it is inaccessible. Entropy has increased.

As we look around and find that every mechanism which shows time asymmetry is of this same basic kind, we must wonder whether this is also true of ourselves. Could it be that these same statistical tendencies which so heavily pervade all our surroundings and, no doubt, our own physical and chemical mechanism, are the ones that give us the time asymmetry of which we are so very conscious? I could certainly see no case for invoking anything different for biology when this biology is in fact placed in the real world that possesses all the asymmetry needed to explain the effect. It seems to me desirable not to make any special explanations for biology when there is no clear need for it. Let us understand as much as we can about biology in terms of the physical mechanisms.

What Makes Order?

We still have to search further, however, before we can understand all this. It is only in systems that have a certain state of order that the asymmetry in time shows up. If a person set it up we can readily understand why it should be ordered. But how is it in nature? If all systems get disordered, then how come that we still have any that are ordered? You might have thought that in the age of our solar system, 5×10^9 years, anything would have gone to the maximum disorder that it could reach. As we have said before, in the example with the heat insulated box, no effect of progressing time would then be in evidence. Why has all this not yet happened?

The situation here is essentially different just because we are not in a heat-insulated box. The radiation can, and does, escape from our locality. Where does it go? Into the depths of space. Just from our system? No; presumably from all other stars it is just the same. A great amount of radiation goes out and only very much less comes in. Our local system did not get to the maximum state of disorder because it could radiate away all the time. Had we had a heat-insulating box around the solar system, all would by now be at a uniform high temperature.

If we want to see the reason for the statistical tendencies on any one scale of things, it seems that we always must look to the next larger scale. Each system we look at is not in practice completely insulated from the rest of the world and it is the outside influences that determine the way things go. When we keep seeing fresh order generated, as for example when water keeps being delivered to the river above the waterfall to have its ordered energy dissipated into heat at the bottom, this is not infringing the general rule that entropy increases. What is happening is that we are not looking at an isolated system and that, for the apparent decrease of entropy, for every apparent ordering of things there is, on some larger scale, a greater increase of disorder. On our lives, the dominant influence is the sun shining radiation into the depths of space. We must think of ourselves and of all the activities around us in which order seems to be regenerated, all those things that are not just running down, all the clocks that are being wound up, all the waterfalls being replenished, as being connected with little heat engines that derive their input heat chiefly from the solar radiation and that are cooled by radiation into space. It is this heat flow from the sun out into space which, by being interrupted a little, can be made to generate order locally, but only at the expense of generating even more disorder on a larger scale. More heat energy is later widely distributed in the universe where before it was concentrated in the sun. This is the greatest disordering and running down process in our part of the world.

A heat engine is able to generate some order, but it needs a source of heat and a sink of heat into which it can reject heat at a lower temperature. You know that for your motor car you have a radiator, and for any other heat engine there is some means of getting rid of heat. Without it, it would all merely heat up to a uniform high temperature and nothing more would happen. In the universe, the largest heat engines are driven by a source of heat, namely the stars, and a sink of heat, namely the cold space. Is it not strange that, after all this time, space is still cold? It seems to be able to accept heat being dumped into it indefinitely without getting hot. What is the explanation for that?

One answer might be that there is just so much space, that all the stars in the time in which they have been shining have not been able to fill it up with radiation. If we went on long enough, then eventually stars and space would all become equally hot and all heat engines would cease. No fresh order could be generated anywhere then, and no processes would then be seen in which there is a gross difference between the two senses of time. We do not have to trouble to explain how people's minds will then single out one sense of time because in that circumstance there would be no people. But so long as space is cold and the heat-flow from the hot stars continues, heat engines can work; all the statistical tendencies that we have discussed will continue to be in existence. These tendencies from which we judge the sense of time are thus clearly related to the overwhelming tendency in the real world for

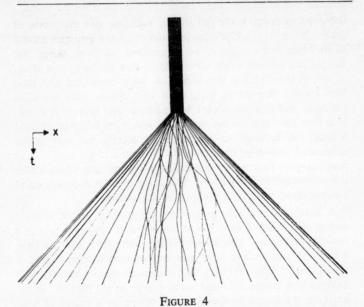

FIGURE 4

*A space-time diagram showing an explosion. This is a common feature
in the all-embracing pattern in the one sense of time, but rarely occurs
in the other sense. Photon clouds often expand but rarely contract.*

radiation to expand outwards into space rather than for radiation
to come inwards and focus on objects. It is this one overwhelming
tendency in the real world that fixes the statistical behaviour of
systems on all other scales, for they all depend on heat engines
that use space as the sink of heat. Clouds of photons, the units
of radiation, have an overwhelming tendency to expand rather than
contract. That seems the most basic statement to be made about
the statistical tendencies in our universe. We have traced the effect
to a property of the universe which it possesses at any rate at the
present time. It is a separate but interesting problem why the
universe has this property.

The Universe as a Heat Sink

You may have heard that one has discovered the universe to be
expanding. What one has discovered is that, as one looks at very

distant aggregates of stars, one observes their light to be a deeper red colour than it would be from similar objects nearby. This effect is just of the kind that would be produced if the distant objects were rushing away from us at a high speed and their light was therefore subject to the Doppler effect which transposes it to a lower frequency.

If the universe is expanding in this way, then we could immediately understand why it does not get filled up with radiation. As fast as radiation is being poured into it, the spaces that contain it increase their volume. It is like pouring water into a barrel which fails to fill up, not because it has a leak but because it is increasing its size all the time.

We can look at the same thing in another way. If we pursued a particular direction of looking far enough into the distance, then, if the universe is big enough and is pervaded by stars everywhere, such a line of sight will eventually end on the surface of a star. But if in each direction of looking we saw the surface of some star, then all the sky around us should be as bright as the surfaces of stars, and everything in it would then be as hot as the stars. This is clearly not the case. Either lines of sight do not all end on the surfaces of stars but just go on forever into nothingness or—and that is the solution more commonly adopted—they end on surfaces of stars mostly only at a very great distance, and at that distance the stars are rushing away from us at a very high speed. As a result the light is so far transposed to low frequencies that it represents no visible light any more and that, in accord with the Doppler effect on light, the energy content of it has become very low. This is saying no more than that a very distant star which is rushing away from us cannot deliver much energy at us because it is spending almost all its energy to put light in transit on this ever-increasing path. The observed expansion of the universe thus gives an explanation for the dark sky, even if the universe does not thin out, and if stars continue as far into the distance as you could ever see.

If we adopt the expanding universe explanation for the dark sky, then a little bit more of the story falls into place. The tendency for radiation to expand rather than contract is then clearly just related to the tendency for matter on a large scale to

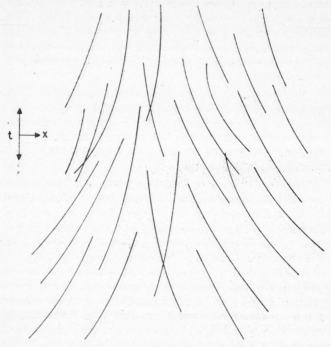

FIGURE 5

A space-time diagram showing that symmetry with respect to the sense along the time axis can be absent, yet the average properties need not be changing. (Time is "homogeneous" but not "isotropic".)

expand rather than contract. The reason for a dark sky was that the space between objects was for ever increasing and that is now precisely the reason why radiation is generally expanding. On a small scale we saw a statistical tendency dictated by the fact that radiation expands. On a large scale we see that this expanding radiation merely follows the expansion of the universe. The radiation is the main link between the large and the small.

Let us look again at a space-time diagram, but now one drawn for a very large scale. World lines of galaxies are now moving apart in the sense in which we normally regard time. Radiation in spaces in between is also moving apart. Now, if we have time-symmetrical laws of physics and we look at this diagram without our native prejudice as to sense of time, we should be able to interpret everything just as well in reverse. A contracting view of this universe would have to be just as acceptable so far as the laws of physics are concerned. If possible we would also like to explain that we would choose to regard this universe as an expanding one.

The Universe in Reverse

What happens if we try to describe the universe in the other sense of time? As you recall, the process of emission and reception of light can be regarded equally in either sense. All the places that in the one sense were the emitters will now become the receivers and *vice versa*. In this reversed picture most radiation would therefore come from such objects as the extensive dark clouds in galaxies, namely the objects which to the normal way of thinking absorb most of the starlight, and from these dark clouds the light would go usually a very long way. In the contracting universe it would then be severely shifted to the blue, and its intensity greatly increased. It would mostly converge onto the surfaces of hot stars and in the view we would then take, it would be the cause of their heat. In the star the heat would go into nuclear transformations that use up energy. All this is no more than merely describing all the radiation moving in reverse in a universe that is itself going in reverse. Now in this universe, the sky is not dark and radiation is generally contracting. All the statistical tendencies, if our previous arguments were correct, would now be in reverse. Disordered systems would tend to order themselves; radiation would tend to converge onto objects and heat them; heat in general would flow from cold bodies to hot bodies and entropy would in general decrease. This is the description of our universe in the opposite sense of time. It sounds very strange but it has no conflict with any laws of physics. If we think of the universe not in terms of an object progressing through time in a certain sense, but, as I have said before, of the existing totality of world lines, if we think of it as the great pattern on the wall of our space-time diagram, then either description is equally valid.

Our strange description is not describing another universe, or how it might be but isn't, but it is describing the very same thing.

You might be puzzled by some features of this. For example, you might say that you know for sure that you are living in an expanding and not a contracting universe. Clearly, you say, when I turn the telescope to look at a distant galaxy it makes its mark on the spectroscopic plate on the red side and not the blue. There is an objective mark on the photographic plate in the place which means expansion and not contraction. There is no mark on the blue side of the spectroscope. Is this not an objective way of describing it? But this argument was not conducted sufficiently carefully. If we regard the universe as contracting then heat flows from cold bodies to hot bodies. All the statistical tendencies are reversed. A cold photographic plate is thus the last place on which to try and find the effects of radiation from a hot body. We need to go to hot places, not cold ones, in order to see the radiation arrive from the depths of space. The surfaces of stars or a flashlight held out of the window, these would be the places that would attract radiation from afar. This view is consistent since the emission and reception of light are indistinguishable processes.

Think of these processes as described on our great pattern on the wall; there is no question of describing things as likely or unlikely. That is the pattern which is there. You may describe it this way or that way in terms of a progressing time and you will then invent in each case the appropriate description of the statistical tendencies, and of the cause-effect relationships. But think of it as a given pattern in which you can recognize certain regularities, namely the laws of physics. The idea of a cause and effect relationship now becomes meaningless. You may see relationships within the pattern which are of the kind that in the conventional description one would be called the cause and the other the effect. In the description with the opposite sense of time you would just have to reverse these roles. But in the timeless description in our pattern on the wall they are only related events but with nothing in the nature of a cause and effect relationship.

Time and Consciousness

Now having arrived this far in the argument, can we understand why in our consciousness we have singled out one peculiar way of describing the little piece of the pattern on the wall of which we have a knowledge? Why is it that instead of a static description of the pattern, or indeed one in the other sense of time, we pretend to know that we are sliding in one particular sense along the time co-ordinate?

We ourselves are, of course, little patches in this great diagram, finite, alas, in all four co-ordinates. What can it mean when we speak of having knowledge of the past? It means no doubt that there is some relationship between world lines interior to us and exterior world lines. Some code has been established, as in a computing machine, between events outside and configuration in our memory unit. Will this relationship be equally close with events displaced in either sense along the time co-ordinate? In each case we have facts at our command, namely the configuration of our memory, and we use them to infer something about the outside world. We say we are "remembering" or that we are "predicting", depending on whether this inference is concerned with the past or the future. It seems to me that our principal notion of the progress of time stems from the fact that these two operations seem so different to us. They are different mainly in the degree of certainty that can be achieved. The past we think we may know without any doubt, but the future is much less certain. Can we now understand where this difference comes from?

In terms of the great pattern on the wall, in which our brain box is represented as a little patch, we would now like to understand that the relationship between the interior of this patch and the outside is closer in the direction that we call the "past" than in the direction that we call the "future". Of course all this is placed into a diagram with an overwhelming asymmetry with regard to the two senses along the time co-ordinate. We are concerned with the world lines of a very large number of particles and for that reason, statistical probabilities become nearly certainties. The difference in the statistical tendencies of looking along the pattern in one sense or the other then appears a difference in principle and not merely a change of probabilities. Our brains can compute the past from their present configuration more accurately than they can compute the future, and because the difference in the quality of this computation is so great, we think of it as a difference in principle. The great pattern has, after all, the quality of spreading out, of diffusing itself, of making things more random in the one sense of time, and therefore it is not surprising that the computation does not work so well in that sense.

If one had the great pattern plotted all one could say from it is that the correspondence between inside and outside the brain box was much closer in the one sense of time than in the other. But as we have said, that diagram would then contain all the information there is. This must be the only reason for developing the notion of the passage of time.

Let us sum up these remarkable conclusions. The real world can be completely described by a pattern of lines in four dimensions where each particle of matter is represented by a line. Because of the large-scale architecture of the universe, that pattern is mostly unsymmetrical with respect to the two senses along one of the co-ordinates. This asymmetry shows up in any region containing a large number of lines but, as we look on a smaller and smaller scale, the asymmetry disappears. We who are parts of this pattern have such a relationship with it that we create the fiction of a "time" which for ever progresses and which transports us along with it.

It may be very difficult for us to change our ways of thought. Even as I explain all this I am thinking that these lectures have come nearly to an end, that I have already said most in the past and that I will only say a little bit more in the future. I don't really think of myself as a patch existing in this great static pattern and of these lectures representing some relationships between the interior of my brain, the air molecules in the room, and the interiors of your brains. I know that I am thinking of it instead as a process in time involving my own free will and decision and influencing the future but not the past. It is hard to do otherwise even though I know I have no justification for this point of view. When we come to discuss physics, however, it may complicate matters to discuss it with concepts that are subjective and have their origin in introspection only. The passage of time is a notion of that kind.

I cannot tell you whether it is important or not to try to understand these matters. Progress in science is often dependent on a new way of looking at things and on finding a less subjective way of describing the exterior world. I do not know whether this will be so here and I suppose most people would say that "only time can tell".

MEN OF SCIENCE

Being especially some of their own utterances in which they speak of their labours, their fears, their travail physical and mental—how they were inflamed with the desire to know and their constant zealousness after Truth—how the Drama and Beauty of Nature stirred them, fired their imagination, aroused their curiosity, kindled their intellect—how their Wonder on the Great Scheme of Things was awakened—how they appraised themselves and their work and how some later giants of the intellect measured what they had done.

by

JULIUS SUMNER MILLER

JULIUS S. MILLER
Professor of Physics, El Camino College,
California.

INTRODUCTION

The great body of knowledge which the human race has gathered up has not come to be by the mystic gyrations of a magical wand. It has not appeared full-grown and in bloom. It has not come up with a suddenness out of the dark as the sun follows the night. It is first of all *the work of men* and more often than not their lives and their labours were clouded and burdened with fear and with travail. The advance of a new idea has ever been fraught with danger and this boldness has cost some their very lives. Now these men of whom we shall tell were all different in their private ways and in their personal histories, as men are and as they must be, but they were also singularly alike and in this way: they were inflamed with the desire to *know*. The Order and Beauty of Nature stirred them in their deepest souls; their intellect was kindled by the Great Drama and Wonder which envelops us all—*why* is the sky blue? *why* is the sunset red? And they were forever possessed by a steadfast zealousness after Truth and a fanatical devotion to their hopes.

So the study of Science and the meaning of Science and the hope of Science take on a new complexion and a new depth *when we know the men who made it*. It is a sorry thing indeed just to know what Copernicus did without ever *feeling* its beauty and its spirit, for this is most easily and nobly accomplished by getting a *feeling* for Copernicus. And this we acquire by having "touch" with Copernicus. With poor instruments and with poor eyesight but with a profound analytical genius and "four times nine years of labour", he unravelled the scheme of things and wrote: "We find, therefore, under this orderly arrangement, a wonderful symmetry in the universe . . . and a definite harmony in the motion and magnitude of the orbs, of a kind it is not possible to obtain in any other way." And it was only on the day of his death that he had in his hands the first printed pages of his *De Revolutionibus Orbium Coelestium*. And his friend and student Joachim Rheticus "filled with eagerness to learn the new system" wrote—having learned it—"For all these phenomena appear to be linked most nobly together, as by a golden chain . . . bearing witness that the earth **moves**." And soon upon its publication we have the tragedy and drama of Giordano Bruno who, for praising the work of Copernicus, was burned at the stake. Is not this "touch" with Copernicus a deep and stirring adventure?

Now again, if you will, consider Kepler whose entire life was poverty, ill health and adversity; who suffered threats of imprisonment, the death of his wife and children, the witch trial of his mother. "In the year 1595 I brooded with the whole energy of my mind and soul on the Copernican system . . . There were three things: the number, the size, and the motion of the heavenly bodies . . . I searched zealously for reasons why they were as they were, and not otherwise." With fanatical patience, "Endowed," as Arago said, "with two qualities . . . a volcanic imagination and a pertinacity of intellect," and after a quarter-century of labour, days and nights, he laid down the "harmony of the world". It is again a sorry thing *just to know* Kepler's Laws of Motion, for without a "feeling" for their beauty and the travail which gave them birth they are like lifeless things, all emptiness, cold and void. We must, I say, *feel* about them in the way Kepler did: "I have attested it as true in my deepest soul and I contemplate its beauty with incredible and ravishing delight." Is not our own spirit lifted by this brief "touch" with Kepler?

Or think on Newton who, born a weakling, prematurely, had to wear a bolster about his neck to support his head! And his mother was wont to say that ". . . he was so tiny I could put him in a quart mug". Now *all* that Newton did—his Laws of Motion, his Theory of Gravitation, the invention of the Calculus, the nature of white light—*he did in two years*. He wrote: "All this was in the two plague years of 1665 and 1666, for in those days I was in the prime of my age for invention, and minded Mathematicks and Philosophy more than at any time since." But is it not regrettable that the study of these things in the school and in the university is viewed by so many as a chore and a burden to be done? It would not be that, I say, if a "feeling" and a "passion" for Newton were aroused. For when Newton says: "Whence is it that Nature doth nothing in vain; and whence arises all that order and beauty which we see in the world?" must not our own intellectual flame be awakened?

And so my case is clear. What we need in the schooling at all levels and in every subject is more history, more biography, more humanism, more anecdote. For science especially, my case is very strong, for in the study of science these ingredients are shamefully wanting. Whatever science is, it is first of all *human adventure* on the highest intellectual grounds revealing constantly the great spirit of questioning and wonder which prevail in the human mind. In science proper lie the noblest aspects of man, the highest goals, the deepest hopes for things eternal. For this intellectual process has one singular intention, one noble ambition, and it is this: *to uncover the orderly Beauty of Nature*. With this comes the great satisfaction of **understanding** which must indeed rank as the highest ambition of man.

And so it is that Science, when viewed properly, in its noblest flights, in its deepest attributes, is indeed one with Religion for there ever remains the sphere of Darkness beyond our reach. It is as with Newton that the great ocean of Truth lies all undiscovered. And when for the man of Science imagination and intellectual inventiveness are fired by curiosity and inflamed by the desire to know, he weaves from the facts of Nature our material and spiritual life.

It is as Pope says: "The proper study of mankind is man." And in this same way is the study of Science inspired and exalted.

Julius Sumner Miller.

El Camino College, California, U.S.A.

PREFACE

It has been my custom for some 30 years in the classroom to "illuminate" the subject of the lecture with some remarks historical, biographical, humanistic, anecdotal. There is no gainsaying the virtue of this. The evidence is laid out in the preceding pages called Introduction. Must not one be really "dead" who sits before me unmoved when I tell him that Robert Hooke announced his Law of the Spring in 1676 in this very peculiar way: *ceiiinosssttuu?* Or that Euler, when he lost his right eye at age 28 made this utterance: "J'aurai moins de distractions"[1]? Whenever possible I have shown a picture of the man. Now there is available another scheme which adds beauty and colour. It is noteworthy that the countries of the world have seen fit to honour men and events of science on postage stamps, not only their own nationals but men of achievement everywhere. And so we have France and Poland honouring Isaac Newton—but England has not! Japan honours René Laënnec on his invention of the stethoscope; Rumania, Turkey and Russia honour Ben Franklin; Argentina honours William Harvey and Ivan Pavlov; Monaco honours the Curies. And with proper allegiance, Italy honours Galileo, Volta, Galvani, Leonardo, Avogadro, Torricelli, and Greece honours Pythagoras. Some of these stamps I have purchased but not with any special interest in philately. These I have photographed in colour and the transparency projected on the screen in a darkened lecture room reveals the great beauty and detail of the engraving. We have then before us, so to speak, the man in the flesh, and this is a point of departure for remarks historical and humanistic, biographical and anecdotal.

In the following pages I offer you some of this adventure. It is not my intention in any degree to write a history of science nor to relate biography in the usual way. Books on the history of science abound as do biographies and I would urge students at all levels to read far and wide in these. It is in the young formative years that these things are most likely to have their greatest impact

---

1. "I shall have fewer distractions."

173

and the whole life of a boy or girl may be turned by the printed page. History is full with such events. Or one may be led to do an experiment which changes the course of history. When the great Lord Rutherford was asked, in his later years, "How, Sir, did *you* come into physics?" he replied: "When I was a little boy in my native New Zealand I was charged with the tending of sheep and one day when things were quiet I picked up a stick and put it into a pond of water, and it was bent—and when I pulled it out it was straight—and when I put it into the water again it was bent again! Make a fellow think, wouldn't it?"

So there appears on these pages, the picture of a stamp or several pictures, and with each I give some brief recitation. It is important, in my view, to note the national origin of the man for we must be ever mindful that no single people has any special claim to the intellect. Such a distorted view has no foundation. We label a man French or Italian or Greek or Polish simply for the purpose of showing how wide-spread, how belonging-to-all-the-world, this devotion to the intellectual life has been. Consider that noble array—Copernicus the Pole, Tycho Brahe the Dane, Kepler the German, Galileo the Italian, Newton the Englishman, and now Einstein the Jew. It was this fantastic array of intellectual giants of diverse national origin who, over a span of some 500 years, fixed forever the great scheme of the Firmament. It is like the invitation which Leibniz made "to others more penetrating . . . to join the beauty of their minds to the labour of mine".

We give also the dates of birth and death, not as some dry, dead, isolated fact to remember but rather to mark his place in the large historical view. It is significant, for example, that after Ptolemy in the 2nd century A.D., no important advance was made in astronomy until Copernicus more than 1000 years later. And it was nearly 2000 years after Archimedes that the Dutchman Simon Stevin advanced the subject of Mechanics. Or, to take another view, Galileo was born on the day the great Michelangelo died and Galileo died in the year of Newton's birth. How might we appraise these things? Maybe it was now destined that Italian science transcend Italian art and that Newton carry on the Great Plan established by Galileo.

174

On matters biographical I write sparsely. What I relate is, I hope, now delightful and enchanting, now sadness and sorrow, my purpose constantly being to arouse a "feeling".

It is my conviction that we come closest to the soul and mind of the man *when we hear him* with his own words. Accordingly, quotations appear abundantly. These must be read with feeling, with emotion, with proper inflection, with the image of the man in mind. And they should be read **aloud**, with gesture of hand and flail of arm, to yourself or to someone who listens with eager attention. In this way the man comes alive. In this way you *hear* him. Listen to Leonardo on the flight of birds: "Why should man not be able to do what the birds do?" Or again: "Thou, O God, dost sell unto us all good things at the price of labour."

What each one of these strange creatures of human kind accomplished—for indeed they were strange and uncommon men—must be viewed as a great and singular event for in the largest sense it awakened new thought, gave history a new direction and life a new horizon. Indeed, it changed the world!

And so it is my great hope that what you read here in these brief little "stories" will have much meaning and inspiration. There is certainly among you another Michael Faraday or a Marie Curie and it is my singular ambition that we discover you.

J.S.M.

MEN OF SCIENCE

I

PYTHAGORAS

Greek; c. 582-500 B.C.

In the time of Pythagoras the writing of history had not yet begun so that little is known of his life. He may have been the pupil of Thales. It is known that he left Samos to escape the tyranny of the King, Polycrates, and that he travelled far—to Egypt, Phoenicia, Chaldea, Palestine, India. At Crotona, the ancient Greek republic on the Gulf of Taranto, he established his secret brotherhood known as the Order of the Pythagoreans. The membership was of two classes, "probationers" and mathematicians, and their ambition was to spread holiness and teach mathematics. During his lifetime and after his death the condition of membership was this: that all discoveries must be attributed to the Master Pythagoras. Any who claimed for his own glory any discovery was forthwith charged with impiety and the penalties were severe. One Pythagorean, Hippasus, a geometer, claimed that he had discovered how to circumscribe a sphere about a dodecahedron and he was drowned at sea! The Order flourished for at least two decades but strife within their ranks brought many to a violent end.

To the Earth-Air-Fire-Water doctrine of the early Greek philosophy the Pythagoreans added the abstract idea of Number. This was a great contribution for it elevated Mathematics above the mere practical and gave us such foundational elements as axioms, postulates and definitions. They recognized irrational numbers such as the diagonal of a square, gave us a proof of the sum of the angles of a triangle, and bequeathed to us that famous theorem which became the 47th proposition of Euclid.

Strangely enough, they viewed the Earth as a globe and "suspected" its motions and it was this very doctrine that led Copernicus to his heliocentric ideas.

The Pythagoreans found the role of number in the behaviour of vibrating strings—that the length of a string governs its pitch and that strings with lengths in the ratio 2:1 gave notes an octave apart. They thus gave music its mathematical foundation.

Theirs was the first "scientific society", the forerunner indeed of scientific academies like the Accademia del Cimento of Florence in 1657, the Royal Society of London in 1662, the Académie des Sciences of Paris in 1666. The role of scientific societies and scientific academies can hardly be exaggerated and their history is filled with drama and intrigue.

The motto of the Pythagorean Brotherhood was a noble one indeed:

> *"A figure and a step forward;*
> *Not a figure and a florin."*

Which brings to mind the following: A student of Euclid had just learned the first proposition whereupon he turned to his Master and said: "And what shall I profit by learning these things?" To this Euclid called his slave and said: "Give him a coin for he must make gain out of what he learns."

The Badge of the Order was a pentagram:—So, join us; wear

this symbol of your piety and remember, all that you discover must be credited to the Master!

These stamps were issued to commemorate the 2500th anniversary of the founding of the first School of Philosophy by Pythagoras of Samos. The Pythagorean Theorem is recognized at once; the other shows a Samos coin picturing Pythagoras with a cylinder surmounted with a sphere.

II

DEMOCRITUS

Greek; c. 460-370 B.C.

Of his life and death little is known but the reputation of Democritus of Abdera stands from antiquity, solid as rock. He was most certainly the pupil of the philosopher Leucippus who in turn with Empedocles and Anaxagoras were pupils of Zeno. It was Zeno, you will recall, who was troubled with the problem of motion and thus we have *Zeno's Paradox*. Throughout his life Democritus showed a tireless zeal for knowledge and he developed his scheme of empty space and material "atoms"—a view nearly identical with our views today. So, nearly 25 centuries later we read this on the nature of matter:

"Matter contains solid particles with empty spaces
between. These solid bits we call atoms. These
atoms are hard, indivisible, indestructible. They
are in continual motion. Different atoms in
number, size and array make up different things."

In our 20th century description of matter we can hardly do better! In solid stuff like a stone, say, Democritus has the atoms rather in a feeble motion whilst in a fire they dance about more wildly. Now this view of "atoms" was a wonderful idea but Democritus carried it a bit too far. He thought the soul was also composed of atoms. This view was odious to Plato and to Aristotle, and Dante in his time assigned Democritus to a very low level of Hell! This was the fitting penalty for such impiety.

The view of Democritus must stand, however, as one of the great philosophical achievements of antiquity. To our great fortune his theory of matter was immortalized in verse by Titus Lucretius Carus—known simply as Lucretius—that great Roman poet of the 1st century B.C. Lucretius was a contemporary of Caesar and Cicero. This poem *"De Rerum Natura"* ("Concerning the Nature of Things") is most certainly the greatest "scientific" poem of all time. It is indeed little short of amazing to find in it our very own ideas on the structure of matter:

> "There are certain bodies which cannot be rent
> apart by blows . . .
> Some things are held together by rings and
> hooks . . ."

And so it is in our own day that "certain bodies cannot be rent apart" and as for "rings and hooks" what better can we say?

III

HIPPOCRATES

Greek; c. 460-377 B.C.

The Age of Pericles was the Golden Age of Greece. All the noblest virtues of human kind came forth: government, law, public works, history, drama, philosophy, science. The spirit of the age found its highest expression in the creation of the beautiful of which the Parthenon is the classic example. It was this Age which produced Herodotus, the Father of History, Sophocles the dramatist, and Hippocrates.

Hippocrates of Cos is the most celebrated physician of the ancient world. Nearly one hundred works bear his name. Not only did he gather up all that was sound in the history of medicine but he gave significant evidence of the scientific spirit in his own writings. In these days of which we speak, the sick sought divine healing in the temple where disease was cast out by charms and prayer. Hippocrates abandoned magic and superstition and practised observation and experiment.

His recommendations for the handling of sewerage and the practice of sanitation were the first of their kind. Strangely enough, it was even in his day that physicians were supported by the public purse to treat citizens free of charge. As Ecclesiastes says: ". . . and there is no new thing under the sun."

His greatest contribution was the concept that disease is not caused by things supernatural but by real things. "Every sickness has a natural cause and without natural causes nothing happens." So too, "Nature is the best physician."

It is certain from what Hippocrates said that he practised his medical art knowing well the role of drugs and surgery and cauterization. "Where drugs fail the steel will cure; where the steel fails the fire will cure; where the fire fails there is nothing that can cure."

Coupled with his great skill as a physician he possessed nobility of character and the highest ethical ideals. These have come to us in the celebrated Oath of Hippocrates, reverently subscribed to by men of medicine in all of history. This exposition stands indeed as a monument forever.

> *"I swear by Apollo the Physician, and Aescula-*
> *pius, and Hygeia and Panaceia, and all the gods*
> *and goddesses, that according to my ability and*
> *judgment I will keep this oath . . .*
> *I will give no deadly medicine to anyone even*
> *if asked nor will I ever suggest such counsel . . .*
> *Whatever house I enter I will come for the*
> *benefit of the sick and will avoid every act of*
> *corruption . . . Whatever I see or hear in the*
> *lives of men which should not be heard abroad*
> *I will not divulge knowing that all these things*
> *must be kept secret . . ."*

The writings of Hippocrates are filled with aphorisms:

"Persons who are very fat are apt to die earlier
than those who are slender . . .

Old persons endure fasting more easily than
young . . .

A chill when with a sweat is bad."

The stamp shows a statue of Hippocrates and reads "Hippocrates
of Cos". It was issued to commemorate the return of the
Dodecanese to Greece. Is it not wonderful that Greece commemorates this historical event with such a tribute to her honoured
man of medicine?

Note: There is another Hippocrates, Hippocrates of Chios, a
mathematician. He is credited with the proof by *reductio ad
absurdum*, the theorem that the areas of circles are proportional
to the squares of their diameters, and a remarkable work on lunes.
Euclid drew heavily upon him and Book III of Euclid's *Elements*
may indeed be the work of Hippocrates.

IV

AVICENNA

Arabian-Persian; 980-1037 A.D.

Science had its dawn in the ancient worlds of Babylonia, Assyria and Egypt. Then all the streams of knowledge converged on Greece where for the first time and in a manner unparalleled, a people was smitten with the passion for Truth. Here were born love of knowledge for its own sake and the sovereign efficacy of Reason, and these alone brought forth the Golden Age. With the subjugation of Greece by Alexander, Alexandria became the centre of the learned world. Then came the Roman Age with little achievement in science for their interest in it was almost nil. With the end of the mighty Roman Empire came the great span of a thousand years of darkness and the intellectual life faded away into the Dark Ages. These have been called the Middle Ages.

Now while European learning was at its lowest ebb great events were happening far to the East. The Arabs, under the stimulus of Mohammed, gathered up the nearly-lost and forgotten stores of Greek knowledge. They patronized learning with a feverish intent and from this came forth the Arabian School. Thus while Europe slept, learning had found refuge among the Mohammedans. While in the Christian world things were decaying, Islamic science was coming forth. The singular service of the Arabs and their great contribution was just this: that they kept alive and preserved the interest and the discoveries of their Greek predecessors. And in addition to this absorption of the Greek ideas the Arabs carried them to further heights with their own genius. The most striking work was done in alchemy, the forerunner of chemistry, and in medicine. In this work the name of Avicenna—or, in the Arabic, Ibn Sina—stands pre-eminently.

Avicenna was a genius. Sarton ranks him as the most famous of all Islam. While still a youth he was celebrated in medicine and the story is told that having cured a certain caliph of a terrible disease he asked as reward that he be allowed use of the Royal Library. He travelled throughout Asia pursuing his labours literary and scientific. He wrote treatises on everything that was then known, altogether some 200 books.

His great medical work was his *Canon—Canon Medicinae*—a vast compendium of medicine which was a codification of all the ancient and Muslim knowledge. So great an achievement was this that it was used as a textbook in European universities up to the middle of the 17th century. In Mohammedan countries it is still used as a medical authority! He was especially skilled in the preparation of drugs.

His *Metaphysics* and *Logic* also exercised powerful influence but these met with stiff opposition from the Mohammedan orthodoxy. For this impiety Avicenna suffered some years in prison.

The Persian stamps commemorate Avicenna and were issued on the reconstruction of his tomb at Hamadan. The Afghanistan stamp commemorates the founding of the Afghanistan Faculty of Medicine.

V

LEONARDO DA VINCI

Italian; 1452-1519

In 622 Mohammed fled from Mecca to Medina. In 641 Alexandria fell to the Arabs. European learning was at its lowest ebb in that great hollow called the Middle Ages and in this time the great Arabian School flourished. In 1097 the great expeditions known as the Crusades set out to wrest Jerusalem and the Holy Land from the Mohammedan infidel. Through these Crusades the intellectual outlook of Christian Europe was awakened and by the 13th century a new spirit was rising. Although Scholasticism under Aquinas delayed the liberation of scientific thought from theology — its grip was long and intense — an intellectual atmosphere was coming up afresh, with a revolt against the power of the Church. It was Duns Scotus and William of Occam and Roger Bacon who first shook the foundations of Scholasticism. A new page was turned in the history of the world and the ground was laid for the Renaissance.

In this revival Italy was the centre. There came in quick succession, with enormous strides in humanism, Petrarch and his classical Latin, Erasmus with his war on monastic illiteracy and the abuses of the Church, and Dante. The compass came on the scene and with it the discovery of the earth—Henry the Navigator, Columbus, Magellan. Maps were made by Mercator. It was the Golden Age of geographical discovery. The oceans were conquered. The Reformation under Martin Luther reformed the doctrine of the Catholic Church and out of it came the Protestants. Of all the events, of all the discoveries, the most pregnant was certainly the art of printing, a turn in the history of mankind. Science, especially astronomy, and mathematics, blossomed forth. That singular team of Tartaglia, Cardano, Ferrari and Bombelli gave creative algebra its first blood. Then came Copernicus, Tyche Brahe, Kepler and Galileo. Then also Vesalius, the Belgian anatomist, and William Harvey. The clock, the telescope, the microscope opened up the nature of Nature in scale large and small. Napier invented logarithms. Scientific academies were born. It was indeed an age that defies description. Upon this scene came Leonardo.

Anyone who sets out to write a page or so on Leonardo is filled at once with absolute frustration and despair for no man in the whole history of the world shows such a record. Leonardo took all knowledge for his province and his 5000 pages of notes on subjects of endless diversity make a study of him inexhaustible. Although known best for his art and generally for this alone, his science must be acclaimed. Although he finished little of what he undertook, his conjectures are staggering to contemplate. And this enormous mass of notes and drawings possesses a strange and unheard-of curiosity: his writing is all mirror-writing. To read it one must hold it up to a mirror!

Born out of wedlock at Borgo di Vinci he was apprenticed as a boy to Andrea del Verrocchio, a great artist and an ingenious craftsman of Florence. These were his formative years. At 17 he was accused of a crime of vice and when acquitted uttered this: "The tongue kills more men than the sword." In the 12th year of his apprenticeship Verrocchio died by a fatal chill contracted in the pouring of the metal for an enormous equestrian statue in Venice. Thereafter Leonardo lived on small commissions here and there—the painting of a church tower, the doing of an altar piece. "To Master Leonardo: one keg of wine." At age 30 he offered his services to the Duke of Milan, Lodovico Sforza, as an inventor and military engineer. He said nothing of his artistic ability. "Your Gracious Highness: I have seen and tested the productions of the masters of the art of inventing war machines . . . I shall reveal my own secrets and put them at your disposal." Then followed a catalogue of war machines, siege methods, armoured vehicles and nautical apparatus. But Leonardo was a peace-loving man and justified his war machines by this: "When besieged by ambitious tyrants I find a means of offense and defense in order to preserve the chief gift of Nature, which is Liberty."

So great indeed was his love of peace and liberty and so deep his feeling for living things that he could not bear to see trapped animals and when he met with birds in cages in the village shops he bought them merely to set them free. "The goldfinch," he said, "will carry poison to its little ones imprisoned in a cage—death rather than loss of liberty."

So vast and massive are the works of Leonardo in every quarter of human endeavour that we can do no more than hint at some things he explored. A few quotations will reveal his thinking:

> "Those sciences are vain and full of error which are not born from experiment, the mother of all certainty . . ."
>
> "Nothing is able to move by itself . . . The thing which moves will be made to stop with greater difficulty, the greater its weight . . ."
>
> "The sun does not move . . ."
>
> "Just as the stone thrown into the water becomes the centre and cause of various circles, and the sound made in the air spreads itself out in circles . . ."
>
> "The moon is not luminous in itself . . ."

When the Turks attacked Venice, Leonardo issued an ultimatum: "If you do not surrender within 4 hours we shall send you to the bottom of the sea."

It was, as we know, a sacrilege in those days to open up a corpse and discovery would mean trial, imprisonment or even death. But Leonardo reports on 30 dissections for which he invented his own tools. "All the veins and arteries proceed from the heart." And of the heart he said: "Marvellous instrument, invented by the Supreme Master."

On matters humanistic he had some very beautiful utterances:

> *"Thou, O God, dost sell unto us all good things at the price of labour."*
>
> *"As a well-spent day brings happy sleep, so life well-used brings happy death."*

Leonardo has been abundantly honoured on postage stamps by many countries. The 100-lire stamp reads: "Man with his large wings by beating against the air will be able to dominate it and lift himself above it."

VI

NICOLAUS COPERNICUS

Polish; 1473-1543

Copernicus was born in a remote little village on the Vistula. His first intention was a career in the church but at Cracow he was diverted to medicine. He then gathered up all that the universities at Vienna, Bologna, Padua and Rome had to offer. He mastered the then-known astronomy which led him to say: "Starting thence I began to reflect on the mobility of the Earth."

The geocentric hypothesis of Hipparchus and Ptolemy stood firm supported also by the great authority of Aristotle. Indeed, after Ptolemy in the 2nd century A.D. (100-168) and his famous *Almagest* (meaning in Arabic "the greatest") which embraced all astronomical knowledge, no advance was made in astronomy for more than 1000 years.

So, with poor instruments and poor eyesight but with a genius for analysis and "four times nine years of labour" he unravelled the scheme of things in his treatise titled *De Revolutionibus Orbium Celestium*. Although the manuscript was finished in 1530, the first printed copy did not reach him until he was on his death-bed in 1543. Of it he wrote: "The scorn which I had to fear in consequence of the novelty and seeming unreasonableness of my ideas almost moved me to lay the completed work aside." But what he had uncovered enchanted him. "We find, therefore, under this orderly arrangement, a wonderful symmetry in the universe, and a definite harmony in the motion and magnitude of the orbs, of a kind it is not possible to obtain in any other way."

The opposition was severe; some was scientific but the weight of it was ecclesiastical. If the earth does spin must not bodies thrown up into the air lag behind? The earth is too sluggish to move! It is opposed to Scripture! And what did Martin Luther say of it? "The fool will overturn the whole art of astronomy." Which is indeed what Copernicus did.

In the spring of 1539 a young professor of mathematics at Wittenberg, Joachim Rheticus, learning of the work of Copernicus and "filled with an eagerness to learn the new system", sought out Copernicus and having learned it wrote: "For all these phenomena appear to be linked most nobly together, as by a golden chain . . . bearing witness that the earth moves."

So with extraordinary courage Copernicus put his treatise in the hands of a printer. Mindful of the risk, he dedicated this laborious study to His Holiness Pope Paul III. "Because, even in this remote corner of the world . . . you are considered to be the most eminent man in dignity of rank and in love of all learning . . ." And further in the dedication Copernicus wrote: ". . . so that by your authority and judgment you can easily suppress the bites of slanderers."

In 1584 Giordano Bruno, a Dominican monk, published an exposition supporting Copernicus. Worse still, he debated its merits publicly in all the cities in France, in England, in Germany, and made the sorry mistake of doing the same in Venice to which he returned after fleeing from Rome some years before. By treachery the Inquisition caught him up and the Pope sent him to his death. He was burned at the stake in 1600 on the Piazza dei Fiori steadfastly refusing to retract. There now stands in the Square of the Flower Market in Rome a statue in his honour and one can feel when standing there the flame of martyrdom. So while in 1543 the Church showed some liberal interest in the new astronomy, it silenced Bruno in 1600. Then came Galileo who first was silenced in 1615 and more firmly in 1633. It was not until 1822 that the sun received the formal sanction of the Papacy as the centre of our planetary system.

We must then appraise *De Revolutionibus Orbium Celestium* as the first of three great masterpieces which changed the world, followed in 1632 by Galileo's *Dialogues* and in 1687 by Newton's *Principia*.

The name Nicolaus Copernicus is the Latinized form and many other spellings were used: Niklas Koppernigh, Kopernikus, Coppernic. This last one is the one he himself preferred.

VII

ANDREAS VESALIUS

Belgian; 1514-1564

In the very same year (1543) that Copernicus published his *De Revolutionibus Orbium Celestium* there appeared the masterpiece of Vesalius *De Humani Corporis Fabrica* ("On The Fabric of the Human Body"). It was the beginning of modern medicine. It has been ranked as the greatest work on human anatomy ever done. Sir William Osler called it the greatest medical book of all time.

Vesalius was born in Brussels and later schooled himself by reading. After attending the University of Louvain and the University of Paris he went to Padua where anatomy was already flourishing. He himself had already had a vast experience with cadavers taken by stealth from the cemeteries and gallows in Paris and here in Padua the scientific spirit of the Renaissance was high. He promptly received high honours and at age 23 was Professor of Surgery and Anatomy. While heretofore the professors lectured while seated, with the barbers doing the dissection, Vesalius did his lecturing and dissection standing in the great theatre. The drawings which he made to illustrate his lectures constituted his *Fabrica.*. This very same *Teatro anatomico* still resides in Padua and to stand there instantly transports a man through four hundred years of struggle to seek out the Truth.

The fame of Vesalius spread. He gave lectures at Pisa and at Bologna. Fallopius and Eustachius, hardly less famous than Vesalius himself, supported his teachings. But it was not all calm. He was attacked for his "unholy" demonstrations and the spread of this forbidden knowledge by his students brought abuse upon him. In his last year he took a pilgrimage to the Holy Land and on the return lost his life in shipwreck.

And so it was that Andreas Vesalius was the first who really knew the human body.

> "I have made a complete arrangement in seven books of my knowledge about the parts of the human body . . . in the first book . . . the bones and cartilages . . . the second the ligaments by which the bones and cartilages are linked . . . and then the muscles. The third . . . the network of veins and of arteries . . . the fourth the nerves . . . the fifth the organs for food and drink . . . also the instruments designed by the Most High Creator for the propagation of the species . . . the sixth to the heart . . . the seventh the brain and organs of sense."

> "I am aware how little authority my efforts will

carry by reason of my youth . . . I am still in
my twenty-eighth year . . . and how little I shall
be sheltered from attacks of those old men who
are devoured by envy at the true discoveries of
youth."

VIII

AMBROISE PARÉ

French; 1517-1590

From antiquity to the Middle Ages and
later, surgery was done by barbers and the
practices were inhuman and beastly. For pain
and torture to the human flesh two stand
pre-eminently: Those wounded in battle had
their wounds treated with boiling oil; those
who had an amputation had the wound
cauterized with hot irons. This last was done
even by Hippocrates.

Now there came on the scene in the 16th
century a kindly barber-surgeon who changed this savage practice.
Of plebeian family and hardly schooled in a formal way he
possessed an unusual passion for the welfare of his patients, and
an uncommon honesty and gentleness. His great reputation brought
him to serve common soldiers and kings.

An occasion now arose when Paré was doing service as an army
surgeon on the battlefield. While treating the wounded in the
manner of the day by applying boiling oil to their wounds he ran
out of oil. Gathering his courage, he concocted an ointment of his
own, made of rose oil and yolk of egg. All through the night he
could not sleep thinking about the wounded men whose wounds
he had not cauterized with hot oil. He expected to find them all
dead on the morning after but to his great surprise found that they
had indeed spent a comfortable night with little pain and no swelling.

The others who were treated with the boiling oil were in high fever and their wounds were swollen and painful. Thus was he led to declare that ". . . never again will I cauterize so cruelly the unfortunate wounded".

On another occasion, on the battlefield, he amputated the leg of a soldier. Convinced that tying off the blood vessels was better than cauterization he used his new method. As might be expected he was ridiculed, but the pain and suffering which the injured were spared soon brought him abundant good favour.

Paré travelled much, ever ready to learn from scholars and housewives alike how better to save men from pain. All these things he recorded in his classic *"Journeys in Divers Places"*. His favourite saying was: "Je l'ai panse, Dieu l'a queri"—"I dressed him, God healed him." By all these things he stands as the Father of French surgery.

IX

TYCHO BRAHE

Danish; 1546-1601

The Copernican theory was not wanting for judgment and most was hostile. The scientific opposition was scanty, the ecclesiastical abundant. If, for some, the Ptolemaic system was too complicated, the new one of Copernicus was contrary to logic and the philosophers declared that "the heavy and sluggish earth is unfit to move". Worse still, the ideas are opposed to the Authority of Scripture. To all this Tycho Brahe subscribed and he set himself the task of finding the true paths of the planets, if such there were.

Having connections with the Royal House and the favour of kings, he received in 1576 from Frederick II the Island of Hveen.

Here they built Uraniborg — The Castle of the Heavens — an observatory of lavish and extraordinary extravagance with library, laboratory, workshops, paper-mill, printing press and instruments of unheard-of size and elaborateness and detail. The best craftsmen of the kingdom were engaged—jewellers, smiths and clockmakers. One quadrant, one of many, had a brass scale of 10-foot radius with readings to fractions of minutes. Its size was so great that twenty men had difficulty in moving it. It all possessed a regal opulence unheard of before or since. And there were palatial quarters for assistants and guests.

Here then with unparalleled patience and skill, with unparalleled tenacity and energy, with a remorseless grip on detail, Tycho Brahe gathered his data for 21 years, all without a telescope. And his time measurements were made with wheel mechanisms and sand glasses. He even took into account the refraction of the air. The observations he recorded transcended in massiveness and accuracy anything that had ever been done.

Then Frederick died and Tycho, arrogant and revengeful, made enemies with the regents who were less indulgent with his madness. Tycho left Denmark. Through a connection with Emperor Rudolph he settled in Prague where he built a new observatory. To his staff came young Johannes Kepler who, on the death of Tycho one year later, fell heir to the vast array of data. The fortune of this event—the meeting of Tycho and Kepler—can hardly be appraised. It is one of those uncanny events of history. It brought together the fanatical patience of one kind with the fanatical patience of another—the power of tenacious observation with the power of tenacious imagination. Out of this union came the splendid monument of Kepler's Laws of Planetary Motion. Thus did Copernicus receive at last vindication and honour.

In his early days Tycho lost part of his nose in a duel. Since he dabbled in alchemy, he contrived a metal piece to replace the missing flesh—a concoction indeed of gold and silver fitting his station in life. Rumour soon had it, however, that he suffered much in the fierce Danish winters because these metals were good thermal conductors! His stubbornness and arrogance kept him from using a chunk of wood which would have done admirably. He was, it was said, a great friend of animals, and he had red hair.

X

SIMON STEVIN

Belgian; 1548-1620

The first great work in Mechanics must be credited to Archimedes. This, the first and simplest chapter, was on statics, and it was profound. We must not make light of those things which now appear so trivial and which schoolboys recite so "expertly". The next great advance came some 1800 years later at the hands of Stevinus of Bruges, the Flemish engineer, and his work showed an amazing originality. Its principal virtue lay in this: that for the first time he proposes a "mental" experiment—a "think" question.

On the title page of his *Principles of Statics,* published in Flemish in 1856—*De Beghinselen der Weeghconst*—there appears this figure: The triangle has looped about it an endless chain. The chain must be in equilibrium in any position and the hanging portion is in equilibrium by itself. Hence the chain can never of itself start to slide. If it did perpetual motion would ensue. Further, if the hanging festoon is removed nothing still will happen.

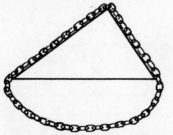

Stevinus was enchanted with his discovery and expressed it so: "Wonder en is gheen Wonder"—"A Wonder and yet it is no Wonder."

Stevin gave us also the condition of equilibrium for three forces acting at a point and thus we have the parallelogram of forces. He proposed the "hydrostatic paradox" and in a most ingenious fashion proves that one pound of water can give rise to a force of one hundred thousand pounds elsewhere! In these matters he anticipated Pascal nearly a century later.

He had something to say also on the subject of falling bodies and describes an experiment: "Take, as Professor de Groot and I have done, two lead balls, one ten times larger and heavier than the other, and allow them to fall from a height of 30 feet on to a plate or other object, upon which they strike with sufficient noise, and it will then be found that they strike the plate at the same moment, so that both sounds seem like one." This stands as the first experimental evidence against Aristotle.

As a military engineer, Stevinus built elaborate fortifications. He also invented a carriage propelled by sails which ran on the seashore carrying 28 passengers faster than a horse can gallop.

It is unfortunate but Stevinus is all too little known.

XI

GALILEO GALILEI

Italian; 1564-1642

There is, in all the annals of science, no single name so well known as that of Galileo, and to think of Galileo we must at once think of Pisa, of Padua, of Florence and of Rome. It was in Pisa

25

where, at age 17 while praying in the Cathedral one day, his attention was gripped by the motion of the great lamp. This he timed with his pulse and from these observations deduced the laws of the pendulum. "Thousands of times I have observed vibrations, especially in churches where lamps suspended by long cords have been inadvertently set in motion . . . But I never dreamed of learning . . . "

In Padua he made his first thermometer and here also his first telescope. ". . . a rumour came to our ears that an optical instrument had been wrought by a Dutchman, by the aid of which visible objects, even though far distant . . . were distinctly seen as if near at hand . . . I applied myself to seeking out the theory . . . an end which I attained a little later . . . and I prepared a tube of lead in the ends of which I fitted two glass lenses."

This instrument he turned upon the sky. It was an event singular and unique in the history of man. On the title page of his *Sidereus Nuncius (The Messenger of the Stars)* he wrote: "Revealing great, unusual, and remarkable spectacles . . ." Herein he reports the discovery of four planets of Jupiter ". . . never seen from the very beginning of the world". Of the moon he wrote: "It is full of hollows and protuberances . . . lofty mountains and deep valleys . . ." And there came into view stars beyond the range of the unaided eye "so numerous as to be beyond belief".

From Padua went a letter to Kepler which later brought upon Galileo the grim charge of the Inquisition: ". . . for having correspondence with some German mathematician."

"Oh my dear Kepler, how I wish you were here in Padua. What a hearty laugh we could have together. I have invited the principal professor of philosophy to look through my glass at my newly discovered moons of Jupiter, which he steadfastly refuses to do. And consider the professor of philosophy at Pisa who by his magical incantations before the Grand Duke hopes to drive my new planets from the sky."

It was at this time that Cosimo de' Medici, the Grand Duke of Florence, ambitious to have his Court flower in science, invited Galileo to his patronage. Here Galileo taught the Copernican astronomy. It brought him at once the censure of the Church. In 1615 he was warned; a year later he travelled to Rome to put his views before the Papal Court. This brought a spell of quiet. In 1630 he completed his *Dialogues Concerning Two New Sciences*. It was his last work, the labour of thirty years, and, as he himself said of it ". . . being superior to everything else of mine". It is the conversation of three characters: Sagredo supporting the Copernican theory and the new physics—most certainly Galileo; Salviati, an intelligent layman; Simplicio, a rather ambitious Aristotelian. It was published in 1632. Galileo was soon called to Rome. Despite his pleading ill-health he was forced to journey to the Eternal City and there he stood trial for heresy and was compelled to recant. The charge of the Inquisition and the Recantation of Galileo stand as eloquent evidence of the travail men endure in their search for Truth.

Condemned to the formal prison of the Holy Office, Galileo returned to Florence, settled in Arcetri, and lived out his last years in increasing blindness and ill health. His days were spent mostly in bed, with Torricelli and Viviani and his son Vincenzio close by. In the Palazzo Orsini in Genoa resides a painting by Niccolò Barabino showing the Master in bed demonstrating a problem with his scholars intent nearby. After he had lost his sight he was visited by Milton who speaks of this in *Paradise Lost*. And in his *Areopagitica* Milton wrote that persecution "had dampt the glory of Italian wits that nothing had been there writt'n now these many years but flattery . . ." And there it was that Milton ". . . found and visited the famous Galileo, grown old, a pris'ner to the Inquisition for thinking in Astronomy otherwise than the Franciscan and Dominican Licensers thought".

In the Chiesa di Santa Croce in Firenze stands the tomb of Galileo. Atop an immense marble sarcophagus is the head of Galileo in massive marble. In his right hand he holds his telescope, his left is on the earth; he looks to the sky. Here rests *Galilaeus Galileius Patric. Flor.* who was born the day Michelangelo died and who died the year of Newton's birth. Thus it was that Italian art was now transcended by the glory of Italian science.

The stamps show (1) Galileo teaching at Padua. The lecture platform seen here still stands. As one sits before it the voice of Galileo is heard: ". . . and down this plane I now roll a hard, smooth and very round bronze ball." We are reminded of the words of Immanuel Kant: "When Galileo rolled a ball down an inclined plane a new light burst upon all investigators of Nature." (2) Galileo presenting a telescope to the Doge of Venice. (3) Galileo with his first telescope in hand. (4) Galileo at Arcetri.

XII

JOHANNES KEPLER

German; 1571-1630

There is in the history of science no case like Kepler's for poverty, ill-health and adversity. As a child he was sickly, his family was poor, his marriage unfortunate. In his worst days, death took his first wife and three children; when he married a second time, death took two more. His mother was charged with witchcraft and dragged from her home in the dead of the night. But with all these burdens his mind remained unfettered for the task he set himself.

His first studies were theological but in 1594 he learned of the Copernican hypothesis: "There were three things in particular—the number, the size, and the motion of the heavenly bodies, as to which I searched zealously for reasons why they were as they were and not otherwise." In 1602 he fell heir to the vast data which Tycho Brahe had gathered up and he succeeded Tycho as Imperial Mathematician at Prague. To the study of this massive record he gave unceasingly twenty-two years of labour. "He was," said Arago, "endowed with two qualities . . . a volcanic imagination and a pertinacity of intellect." And of him Einstein spoke in this warm phrase: ". . . a sensitive personality, passionately devoted to the quest for deeper insight . . ."

His first knowledge of the Copernican system—its mathematical simplicity and harmony—gripped him. "I have attested it as true in my deepest soul and I contemplate its beauty with incredible and ravishing delight."

Convinced that God had made the world on mathematical foundation, he conjectured that the motions of the celestial bodies must be regulated by simple laws. This conviction was the inspiring force of his life. The restrictions of circular orbits led him to consider the ellipse. He also abandoned uniform motion. On the path of Mars alone he spent six long years! Out of this tenacity—out of this conviction—thwarted by a thousand fruitless attempts, the Truth was unfolded.

> "Nothing holds me; I will indulge my sacred fury. The die is cast; I have written my book. It will be read either in the present age or by posterity, it matters not which; it may well await a reader, since God has waited six thousand years for an interpreter."

> "The intense pleasure I have received from this discovery can never be told in words . . . I tired of no labour . . . I shunned no toil of reckoning, days and nights spent in calculation, until I could see whether my hypothesis would agree with the orbits of Copernicus or whether my joy was to vanish in thin air."

Beset by family travail, religious hostility, financial peril, the Thirty Years War, and the death of his patron Emperor Rudolph, Kepler's last years were grim and forbidding. He wandered about teaching and practising astrology so that he could eat. On his last long journey on horseback, ill-fed and ill-clothed, he fell sick with fever and exhaustion and died, November 15, 1630. No trace of his grave exists.

XIII

WILLIAM HARVEY

English; 1578-1657

When Galileo was teaching at Padua, William Harvey was there studying medicine and anatomy. From both came revolutionary ideas which changed the world. At the hands of Galileo experiment was made inviolate and a new way to seek the Truth was unfolded. And in his Preface to the classic *Exercitatio Anatomica de Motu Cordis et Sanguinibus in Animalibus* ("Anatomical Essay on the Motion of the Heart and Blood in Animals") Harvey again spoke the spirit of the new philosophy: "I profess to learn and to teach anatomy, not from books, but from dissections; not from the positions of philosophers but from the fabric of nature."

In the course of his dissections Harvey was led to contemplate the mechanism of the heart and the flow of the blood. When he had laid open the chest of a living animal he observed that ". . . the organ is seen now to move, now to be at rest". And "I frequently and seriously bethought me, and long resolved in my mind, what might be the quantity of blood which was transmitted . . ." When he then made some calculations on the beat of the heart and the number of pulses and the weight of the blood driven by a single pulse, he at once witnessed the astonishing truth: ". . . we have a larger quantity than is contained in ˌthe whole body . . ."

Thus it was that Harvey ". . . began to think whether there might not be a *motion*, as it were, in a circle". And soon he reported: "Now this I found to be true . . . This means that the blood circulates . . . and so on incessantly while life lasts."

Thus did Harvey's name become the greatest name in English medicine. But it was not without travail and opposition for what he declared was rejected altogether by the men of medicine.

As physician to the King, Harvey's official duties included the examining of suspected witches. In not a single case did he report "signs" of commerce with the devil!

XIV

RENÉ DUPERRON DESCARTES

French; 1596-1650

As a boy Descartes was in delicate health and he received from his Rector permission to lie abed as late as he pleased. He clung tenaciously to this special dispensation and throughout his life spent his mornings in bed! And he claimed that the silent meditation which this permitted was the source of his philosophy and his mathematics. His course in life was directed, so he asserted, by a dream wherein he put the question: *"Quod vitae secatabor iter?"* — "What way of life shall I follow?"

Although Descartes was an ingenious and original worker in optics, in music and anatomy—"Here are my books," he said, pointing to the animals which lay before him dissected—his great strength was in logic and in mathematics. "I was especially delighted with the mathematics on account of the certainty and evidence of their reasonings." Philosophy and letters were to him weak, contentious and disputable. Even in those things that had been cultivated for many years by the most distinguished men he found ". . . not a single matter within its sphere which is still not in dispute, and nothing, therefore, which is above doubt . . ."

And so Descartes abandoned the study of letters not without a sovereign command, however, of what had been written. He turned his mind to geometrical analysis and algebra but even here he claimed there was much "either injurious or superfluous". His constant effort was to sift the true from the false. ". . . and it is almost quite as difficult to effect a severance of the true from the false as it is to extract a Diana or a Minerva from a rough block of marble . . ."

We are now in the middle of the 17th century. We have seen the reception given the work of Copernicus and Galileo. How were things now? Are men free to think? Can thought be spoken without the danger of chain and fetter? In 1633 Descartes wrote his physical theory of the universe, *Le Monde*—The World. He was about to publish it when, on a journey to Leiden, he heard the news of Galileo's penalty and suffering. He exchanged notes on the matter with his friend Father Mersenne. Reflecting on this, Descartes put his own work aside with instructions to publish it only after his death.

In 1637 there came from his hands his *Discours de la Méthode pour bien conduire sa raison et chercher la vérité dans les sciences"* —Discourse on the Method of Good Reasoning and of Seeking Truth in Science. His treatise *La Géométrie* was an appendix. In this he presents his analytic geometry and theory of equations. Strangely enough, he wrote intentionally in an obscure way, omitting here and there and often, the necessary analyses ". . . so as to leave to posterity the pleasure of discovering them". It was his essential contribution to mathematics—the beginning of co-ordinate geometry, the recognition of the equivalence of an equation and its geometric locus.

In 1649 Queen Christina, in her imperious way, invited Descartes to the Swedish Court to be her tutor. She was then 19, and she sent a warship to fetch him. The lessons came at 5 in the mornings, even in the rigor of the winter, and in the chill of the palace Descartes was struck in the lungs and died.

"I have often wished," he said, "that I were equal to some others in promptitude of thought, or in clearness and distinctness of imagination, or in fullness and readiness of memory."

His whole life and philosophy and thought is summed up in this single phrase: "I looked for no other advantage than to accustom my mind to nourish itself upon truths and not to be satisfied with false reasons."

In the Latin form his name is Renatus Cartesius—and thus we have the adjective *Cartesian*.

XV

OTTO VON GUERICKE

German; 1602-1686

Unlike many of the early men of science who were born into poverty and adversity and thwarted always by straitened circumstance, Otto von Guericke was, as Scott would say, "Born in the patrician file of society". He was an aristocrat, not a plebeian, and a "finished gentleman". As befitting his station he studied law at Leipzig and at Jena and at Leyden. But in the Thirty Years War his village of Magdeburg was ravaged and the family lost all but their very lives. Now penniless, he devoted himself to learning and as burgomaster of Magdeburg rebuilt the town.

He had heard some lectures on science in Leyden and one of the problems much discussed was this: Is it possible to produce empty space? His first adventure was with a water pump connected to a cask of water. If the water is pumped out, must not empty space remain? So three stout men worked the pump but "a noise was heard in all parts of the cask as if the water was boiling furiously". Air had leaked in through the walls of the cask. He improved on the experiment with a huge copper sphere and after some pumping ". . . the sphere was suddenly crushed with a loud report, and to everyone's alarm . . ." A better-made spherical vessel did not collapse but when the stopcock was opened, ". . . the air rushed into the sphere with such force as if it strove to tear with it a person standing by".

It was in this manner that we had the first air pump or vacuum pump and thus, too, was the dramatic force of the atmosphere first observed. More than this, von Guericke ascribed atmospheric pressure to its weight and concluded that empty space could be only approximately obtained.

Now Otto von Guericke had a fondness for experiments on large scale. He delighted in the astonishment of the people who came from afar to witness his demonstrations. The best known is his Magdeburg Hemispheres which ". . . could only with difficulty be torn apart by a team of eight horses on each side". By request he showed the same to the Emperor with hemispheres one ell[1] in diameter requiring two teams of 24 horses! As every schoolboy must certainly know, *one* team of eight horses would do as well with the other side fixed to a tree, say, but von Guericke was a showman of the first rank.

Von Guericke made also some experiments with a water-barometer and in a public demonstration raised water in an exhausted tube to the third storey of his house. In his *Experimenta Nova Magdeburgica de Vacuo Spatio* in 1672 he reports these great and stirring events which rendered such a quickening to science. But again it must be said that the old doctrines died hard and controversy was strong.

Must it not have been an hour filled with drama and enchantment to witness what went on here?

---

1. An ell is a unit of measurement used in the cloth-making industry. In England it is 1¼ yards, in France, 1½ yards.

XVI

EVANGELISTA TORRICELLI

Italian; 1608-1647

The foundations of modern mechanics were laid in antiquity by Archimedes. Eighteen centuries later Stevinus made his contributions in statics and for the first time proposed a "think" experiment. Then Galileo's science lifted the veil with his astronomical work, his laws of falling bodies, the oscillations of pendula, and projectile motion. This kind of mechanics was now extended to liquids and gases at the hands of Torricelli.

Now Galileo has a close friend, Castelli by name, and Torricelli was his student. As was natural, Castelli put into his student's hands a copy of Galileo's *Discorsi*. Torricelli, stirred by Galileo's mechanics, wrote a memoir on motion and Castelli showed it to Galileo. This led Galileo at once to take Torricelli as his assistant. Until the death of the Master Galileo, Torricelli worked with him— it is perhaps better to say *under* him—and properly enough, Torricelli fell heir to Galileo's position and authority. It is not unlike the "discovery" of Michael Faraday by Sir Humphrey Davy. Moreover, the Grand Duke of Tuscany, impressed with Torricelli's talents, appointed him Royal Mathematician.

Torricelli's work is the first on the motions of liquids, that is, hydrodynamics, as distinguished from the hydrostatics of Archimedes. He discovered the law of flow from a hole in the side of a vessel—the exact relation was formulated by Daniel Bernoulli— and he showed the path to be a parabola. "Liquids which issue with violence from an opening in a vessel have at the point of issue the same velocity which any heavy body would have . . . if it were to fall from the upper surface of the liquid to the opening . . ." He also showed that if the hole is directed upwards from the bottom of the vessel the water leaps up to the same height as the water inside. Since fountains were observed to rise not quite so high he explained the difference by atmospheric pressure from above and the weight of the water pressing down on that coming up.

It was known in Galileo's time that a pump could not lift water more than 34 feet or so. Throughout all of previous history, this was attributed to Nature's abhorrence of a vacuum. Why Nature should regard a vacuum with horror only to this height was never answered, although Galileo proposed that a column of water longer than 34 feet would break under its own weight. Now, asked Torricelli, how high will this *horror vacui* raise mercury? Viviani made the experiment, with a glass tube closed at one end, in the very manner we do it today, and found when he took his finger away at the open end that the mercury stood some 30 inches high. Now, said Torricelli, there is most certainly empty space above, and this came to be known as the Torricellian Vacuum. But now what holds up the heavy column of mercury? The weight of the air, answered Torricelli, and he framed it in this solid phrase: "We live submerged at the bottom of an ocean of air. I assert that the force holding up the quicksilver comes from without."

XVII

BLAISE PASCAL

French; 1623-1662

All people, said Leonardo, fall into three classes: Those who never see, those who see only when shown, and those who see by themselves. No one more properly deserves the last rank than Pascal. In her *Vie de Blaise Pascal,* written by his devoted sister, we learn of this extraordinary man whose life was so brief and so full.

When he was four, his mother died; he had no schooling save by his father and that mostly in conversation. It was his father's practice to have weekly meetings at his home "where all the ingenious men in Paris related their own discoveries or examined those of others". Pascal was allowed to join the conversation and as his sister reports: "My brother stood his ground at these meetings whether in examination or in revealing his own discoveries." Problems came from all of Europe—from Italy and Germany and from all the scholars of France—and young Pascal offered his opinion. The penetration he showed often uncovered details which were obscure to his elders. This meeting was called Académie Libre and it possesses the historic honour of being the forerunner of the Académie des Sciences.

At 12, Pascal wrote a solid essay on sound. He had struck a plate with a knife, the plate sounded but stopped when he put his hand on it. Why did this happen? As his sister wrote: "He wanted to know the reason for everything." At 13, untutored in geometry, he proved the sum of the angles of a triangle with his own axioms and definitions. At 16, he wrote his famous *Essay pour les Coniques.* At 18, his health failed him and he never thereafter had a day free from pain.

Through Mersenne, Pascal learned of Torricelli's experiments and he considered it absolutely crucial to prove that it was the weight of the air that held up the mercury. And if this was so, should not the weight be less on a mountain? His first experiments were in Rouen in 1647. Here, before the city fathers and all the citizens, with tubes 40 feet long or more lashed to the mast of a ship, he found for himself that the water fell to 34 feet. With wine the height was greater! "This knowledge," said Pascal, "can be very useful to farmers, travellers, and others, to learn the present state of the weather and that which is to follow immediately."

What was needed now were experiments on a mountain top. Pascal wrote to his brother-in-law, Monsieur Périer, with instructions to carry out certain experiments on the Puy-de-Dôme, the highest mountain in Auvergne. The exchange of letters between Pascal and Périer are classic and enchanting and full of drama. "I am driven by my impatience to hear of the success of the experiment," wrote Pascal. Périer replied with a full and faithful account with "evidence of painstaking care" carried out in the presence of men "who are as learned as they are irreproachably honest, so that the sincerity of their testimony should leave no doubt as to the certainty . . ." The evidence they saw was wondrous and exciting. Périer wrote: "We were so carried away with wonder and delight, and our surprise was so great, that we wished for our own satisfaction to repeat the experiment . . ." And so they observed that ". . . the height of the quicksilver diminished with the altitude of the site". These great and classic events are beautifully related in the *Récit de la Grande Expérience de l'Equilibre des Liqueurs.*

Little need be said about Pascal's classic Paradox which every schoolboy can recite but it still stands as an intellectual torment for some. Less is known of Pascal's work on the theory of probability which he did in reply to questions from a gambler. But Pascal abandoned science and mathematics—and indeed the world—and turned to religion and letters. It is for his *Letters* that his country sings his praise: "A triumph of literary art of which no familiarity dims the splendour and which no lapse of time can impair." These letters have indeed no equal for eloquence, for clarity or penetration.

And so it is said that Blaise Pascal achieved seven-fold immortality—as a mathematician, a physicist, an inventor, chief creator of his nation's great prose, a theologian, a philosopher, and a fanatic.

XVIII

CHRISTIAAN HUYGENS

Dutch; 1629-1695

By the middle of the 17th century physical thought and inquiry and experiment had unveiled a massive array of problems on the nature of things and many were the subject of despair for these early investigators. But there came on the scene men of extraordinary versatility and genius inflamed with the desire to know. Huygens was one of these and in the ranks of natural philosophy he must be placed beside Archimedes and Galileo and, indeed, Newton.

Huygens' forebears were illustrious in affairs of State, in literature and in music. His father was a brilliant figure in Dutch literature. At 16 young Huygens was diverted from law by his extraordinary talent in mathematics and at 28 had already gained international reputation. He was indeed so highly regarded that when Louis XIV and his famous Minister Colbert established the Académie des Sciences at Paris in 1666, Huygens was invited as the first charter member. He must have shone with uncommon brilliance for other first members were Descartes, Pascal, Fermat and Mersenne, none of whom was mediocre. They all received pensions from the King and palatial quarters.

The first significant accomplishment of Huygens, in association with his brother Constantin, was to grind and polish a lens of such quality that he discovered the rings of Saturn. This settled the classic problem which Galileo had posed. Oddly enough, the discovery was published in a strange and occult form, done this way very likely, to avoid controversy.

In the intellectual atmosphere of the Académie Huygens' genius brought forth in quick succession first his treatise on Mechanics— *Horologium Oscillatorium*—and then the highest flight of his genius —*Traité de la Lumière*. He put forward a clear understanding of that radial force which must be exerted on a particle to keep it moving in circular motion and showed its measure to be mv^2/r. By experiments on a rotating sphere of clay, he suggested that the earth must be flattened. He saw for the first time the dynamical significance of the centre of gravity, created the idea of the centre of oscillation, moment of inertia and equivalent simple pendulum. He also solved completely the problem of the compound or physical pendulum. The solution of this celebrated problem in the dynamics of rigid bodies marks one of the greatest single events in the whole history of mechanics. This, with his theory of evolutes and the cycloid, led to the cycloidal pendulum which is isochronous for all amplitudes.

One of the puzzling problems from before the time of Galileo was collision and impact. Marcus Marci at Prague, a contemporary of Galileo, wrote a treatise titled *De Proportione Motu* (1639) wherein he described the problem known well even to schoolboys. If an array of identical coins or marbles is lined up and one is made to hit one end of the row, one at the far end bounces away. Marci even demonstrated this with cannon balls fired out of a cannon! The Royal Society of London invited solution of this puzzle and Huygens came forward with his *De Motu Corporum ex Percussione*. In this he gave a complete analysis of elastic impact. For the first time we have the concept of mv which, said Huygens, is "une admirable loi de la nature".

Of all the genius of Huygens, his highest flight, as indicated above, was his *Traité de la Lumière*. In this he puts forward his theory of the wavefront and in a most beautiful fashion proceeds to account for reflection, refraction, double refraction and polarization. He got his ideas, he said, by watching the water waves in the canals in his native country. It brings to mind the classic tale of Rutherford with the stick which looked bent.

In 1669 Huygens addressed the Secretary of the Royal Society as follows: "I send you herewith appended, some anagrams which I shall be pleased to have you keep in the registers of the Royal Society, which has been so kind as to approve this method of mine for avoiding disputes, and for rendering to each individual that which is rightly his in the invention of new things." It is not unlike Hooke's communication of his law of the spring in the form *ceiiinosssttuv!*

XIX

ANTON VAN LEEUWENHOEK

Dutch; 1632-1723

In all the history of men of science there is no likeness to Leeuwenhoek. He stands alone. Whereas others had a versatility in their genius, Leeuwenhoek, so it seems, knew only one thing, and that was *to look*. He had a passion for his microscopic observations and revelled beyond belief in the sheer joy of his hobby. He had no schooling but a modest income from a job in his village gave him the leisure to pursue his passion.

The simple microscope has a long history, for magnifying glasses and burning glasses were used by the Greeks and the Arabs. The history of the compound microscope is less certain but it likely had its start with the Dutch. Robert Hooke gave the subject great life and devoted his *Micrographia* in 1665 entirely to observations with the microscope.

Leeuwenhoek's microscopes were all simple—just a lens fixed in a flat brass or silver plate—and the lenses were ground glass beads! Their focal lengths were extremely short and they gave magnifications up to 275 times. They could separate detail one-thousandth of a millimeter apart! And Leeuwenhoek made hundreds of these. He gave 26 of them to the Royal Society "as a mark of his gratitude and acknowledgement of the great honour which he had received . . ." The Royal Society made him a member in 1680 and to this honour he felt duty-bound throughout his life.

Long before his contact with the Society in 1673, he had pursued with ceaseless curiosity these microscopic adventures all of which he recorded painstakingly. Then began his letters to the Society, hundreds of them, in his quaint Dutch dialect. In these he reported a massive array of heterogenous discoveries. He wrote in a warm, colloquial, guileless fashion and with affectionate frankness. His letters, filling four quarto volumes—written over a period of 50 years—are the strangest scientific papers ever gathered. They were put together under the wonderful title *The Secrets of Nature*. (Leeuwenhoek would be grateful for this, the title so fitting his philosophy.)

> "There are little animals in this rain water. They swim! They play around! They are a thousand times smaller than any creatures we can see with our eyes alone. Look! See what I have discovered! They stop, they stand still, they turn themselves around . . ."

He told the Society that he could put a million of these little animals into a grain of sand. The Society scoffed! "The Dutchman says that he has discovered beasts so small that you can put as many of them into one little drop of water as there are people in his native country!" Word spread. Peter the Great came to look and the Queen of England journeyed to Delft to see for herself. Looking at a bit of scum from his teeth he wrote: "There are creatures . . . that go to and fro with the stately carriage of bishops in procession . . ."

So it was that this great human being was the first to see in rain water, in the scum of his teeth, in the spittle from the mouth of a friend, these tiny things alive and never seen before. "No more pleasant sight has ever yet come before my eye than these many thousands of living creatures . . ."

Thus do Leeuwenhoek's "little animalcules" with "motions so swift that 'twas wonderful to see" remain forever in our heritage.

XX

ISAAC NEWTON

English; 1642-1727

In Westminster stands the tomb of Isaac Newton. On the stone floor it reads: *Hic Depositum Est—Quod Mortale Fuit—Isaaci Newtoni.* On the tablet is a longer phrase ending with: "Let men rejoice that so great a glory of the human race has appeared." What did Voltaire say of him? "If all the geniuses of the universe were assembled, he should lead the band." And Edmund Halley in his Ode to Newton wrote: "Nearer to the gods no mortal may approach." And Alexander Pope spoke it so:

"Nature and Nature's Laws lay hid in night;
God said, 'Let Newton be'; and all was light."

Newton was born prematurely on Christmas Day, the year that Galileo died—so tiny, his mother was wont to say, "that I could put him in a quart mug". In his youth he was so weak that he had to wear a bolster to support his neck. As a schoolboy he showed no promise and his mother wanted to make a farmer out of him. Beaten in a schoolboy fight he resolved to outdo his classmates in his lessons and it appears that he did!

At 18 he entered Trinity (1660) and came under the influence of Isaac Barrow, an extraordinary man who at once recognized Newton's genius and resigned his professorship so Newton could have it. In 1665 the Great Plague swept London followed by the Great Fire. The College was closed and Newton returned to the home of his boyhood where he remained in quiet and seclusion for two years. Here "in the solace of lonely meditation" he came to the flowering of his mind.

In the year 1665 he established the binomial theorem, the "direct method of fluxions . . . and the next year, in January, I had the Theory of Colours and in May following, I had entrance into the inverse method of Fluxions . . . and the same year I began to think of gravity extending to the orb of the Moon . . . and found them answer pretty nearly . . . All this was in the two plague years of 1665 and 1666, for in those days I was in the prime of my age for invention, and minded Mathematicks and Philosophy more than at any time since."

Thus it was all that Newton did he did in two years, and these achievements, the calculus, the nature of white light, gravitation, the laws of motion, stand as the most remarkable chapters in the history of human thought. Of all these, it appears that Newton was most pleased with his discovery of the nature of white light: ". . . in my judgment, the oddest if not the most considerable detection which hath hitherto been made in the operations of nature."

His account of this discovery is enchanting:

> "In the year 1666 . . . I procured me a triangular glass prism . . . having darkened my Chamber, and made a small Hole in my Windowshut, to let in a convenient Quantity of the Sun's Light, I placed my prism at its entrance . . . It was at first a very pleasing Divertisement, to view the vivid and intense Colours produced thereby; but after a while applying myself to consider them more circumspectly . . ."

Newton's aversion to publicity and his distaste for controversy

were severe. It was only on the urging of his friend Halley that
he allowed publication at all. He wrote:

> "Make my publication so that it be without my
> name to it for I see not what there is desirable
> in public esteem, were I able to acquire and
> maintain it; it would perhaps increase my
> acquaintance, the thing which I study chiefly to
> decline."

In his *Principia* (which he wrote in 18 months) a stupendous
thing indeed, he made the proofs difficult and obscure "to avoid
being bated by little smatterers in mathematics".

He was extremely absent-minded, given only to the most intense
concentration, unconscious of his sleep, of his meals, of his dress.
On one occasion a friend had come to dinner. The dinner hour
passed. Newton did not appear. The friend sat down, ate the
chicken and put the bones under his bowl. He was about to leave
when Newton came in, apologized for his delay, lifted the bowl
and said, "We have eaten, haven't we?" It was not uncommon for
him to sit on his bed the whole day—thinking. When asked how
he solved his problems and made his discoveries, he replied: "By
always thinking on them." De l'Hôpital, the French mathematician,
once exclaimed: "Does he eat, drink and sleep like other men?"
On the problem of the moon's orbit he once remarked: "I shall
have to give up thinking about the moon for it makes my head
ache."

Alfred Noyes gives us this picture of Newton:

> "Obscure, unknown, the shadow of a man
> In darkness, like a grey dishevelled ghost,
> Bare throated, down at heel, his last night's supper
> Littering his desk, untouched; his glimmering face
> Under his tangled hair, intent and still,
> Preparing our new universe."

He was in his later years Master of the Mint and President of
the Royal Society. This post he held for 20 years being re-elected
every year until his death, such was the great regard for him. In
1705 he was knighted by Queen Anne.

Although he was not on the warmest terms with Hooke he wrote in a letter to Hooke: "If I have seen farther than you and Descartes, it is by standing on ye shoulders of giants."

What Newton thought of himself, he spoke in this stirring and eloquent phrase:

> "I do not know what I may appear to the world
> but as for myself I have been like a little boy
> playing by the seashore ever finding a smoother
> pebble and a prettier shell whilst the great ocean
> of truth lies all undiscovered before me."

> "The main purpose of natural philosophy is to
> argue from p h e n o m e n a without feigning
> hypotheses, and to deduce causes from effects,
> till we come to the very first cause, which
> certainly is not mechanical; and not only to
> unfold the mechanism of the world, but chiefly
> to resolve these and such like questions: What is
> there in places almost empty of matter, and
> whence is it that the sun and the planets gravitate
> towards one another, without dense matter be-
> tween them? Whence is it that Nature doth
> nothing in vain; and whence arises all that order
> and beauty which we see in the world?"

XXI

CLAUS ROEMER

Danish; 1644-1710

One of the great perplexities in physical thought, and it troubled the "natural philo-sophers" for 2000 years, is the speed of light. Empedocles, about 500 B.C., thought it had a finite speed. Pliny in the first century A.D. could say only that it was faster than sound. Roger Bacon in the 13th century would say only that it was too great to measure but was probably finite. Kepler and Descartes thought the propagation of light was instantaneous. The first attempt to measure it was made by Galileo using two observers and two lanterns. It was a significant adventure in the history of physical thought, however little the truth it uncovered.

Now in the 17th century, scientific academies were beginning to flower. A new spirit was a-borning, bold men threw off the fetters of tradition and authority and joined in the pursuit of knowledge. These academies, emancipated from the shackles of the Church, supported experiments, published the discoveries and even sent out foreign expeditions. One of these early journeys was especially significant. In 1671 Jean Picard, one of the astronomer members of the French Academy, went to Denmark to locate the precise position of Uraniborg, Tycho Brahe's observatory. It had already been in ruins nearly one hundred years. Here in Denmark he found Roemer. Roemer returned to Paris with Picard and forthwith became a member of the Academy.

It was with the support of the Académie that Roemer discovered the velocity of light. Thus for the very first time in the history of intellectual adventure do we have experiment and inquiry supported in this way.

Roemer's method is well-known to every schoolboy. Observations on the innermost satellite of Jupiter, which is eclipsed once in each revolution, showed that the period of the satellite was longer when the earth was receding from the planet than when it was approaching. The difference, he deduced, is the time for the light to traverse the diameter of the earth's orbit. His result was low but significant as a discovery. The conclusion that the velocity of light is finite was rejected, especially by the Cartesians. Laplace was stirred by the discovery and was led to speculate on the velocity of gravitation.

In 1678, Huygens delivered his classic essay on the speed and nature of light before the French Academy. He asserted that it has extreme speed but that "light takes time for its passage". He praised "the ingenious proof of Mr. Roemer . . . It is founded upon celestial observations and proves not only that light takes time for its passage, but also demonstrates how much time it takes . . ." So it was that Huygens had proof that the propagation of light ". . . is quite another thing from being instantaneous, since there is all the difference between a finite thing and an infinite . . ."

Thus the great Christiaan Huygens looked to the genius of his Danish colleague Roemer for support of his own conviction.

XXII

GOTTFRIED WILHELM LEIBNIZ

German; 1646-1716

Although Newton alone would have made the 17th century glow with an ever-lasting light, those years had an added glory. It was Leibniz. Even when measured against Newton, Leibniz stands as the most versatile, the most profound, the most prolific among all the thinkers of history. De Quincey called him "The last of the universals". At the age of 20 (this was 1666 and one of Newton's miraculous years) Leibniz already had profound learning in Latin and Greek, in law, in literature, in history, philosophy, theology, logic and letters. Indeed, at 12 he wrote Latin and Greek verse and knew Plato, Aristotle, Herodotus and Xenophon. He commanded the work of Copernicus, Cardan, Harvey, Kepler, Galileo, Descartes, Pascal. His early schooling was indeed a most remarkable kind— and he had but one teacher—Wilhelm himself! Surmounting it all was his mathematical genius. To all this was added boundless curiosity and unending energy and he still had half a century to live!

As is well-known, both Newton and Leibniz are credited with the invention of the calculus. The controversy is now viewed this way: Newton was the first "inventor" of fluxions in 1666 but he did not publish it until 20 years later, in 1687. And Newton's notation was not complete. In 1677 Leibniz, in a letter to Newton, spoke of his own discovery "Which," Newton said, "scarcely differed from my own except in the forms of words and notation." Leibniz published his in 1684, which was three years ahead of Newton. However the credit goes, for this is really unimportant, the mathematics must stand as one of the noblest products of the human mind.

The notation we now use is that of Leibniz. For the *calculus integralis*—the name was suggested to Leibniz by Johann Bernoulli —Leibniz wrote the word *omnia* which he later made the long *S* we now use, meaning *summa*. It is enchanting to note that Leibniz differentiated the product *uv* as $du/dx \times dv/dx$—which would have flunked him in our first course in calculus!

Now late in the 17th century a dispute arose on what is meant by "quantity of motion". Newton took it to be the product *mv*. Descartes was in agreement but Leibniz insisted on mv^2. The problem was this: A body is in motion. Let this motion be opposed by a force. Does the "ability" of the force to arrest the motion depend on *v* or on v^2? The controversy raged for more than half a century, some supporting Descartes, some Leibniz. In 1686 Leibniz opened fire on the issue with a treatise bearing the ominous title: *"A short Demonstration of a Remarkable Error of Descartes and Others, Concerning the Natural Law by which they think the Creator always preserves the same Quantity of Motion; by which, however, the Science of Mechanics is totally perverted."* With this the controversy raged more severely. It was not until 1743—57 years later—that d'Alembert showed that both are right! The disputants, he said, were talking about different things! And so indeed we know that that the product *Fs* is one thing and the product *Ft* another. One measures the energy of the body; the other the momentum. A bullet shot into a wooden block makes the matter clear: The *time* to bring the bullet to rest depends on momentum; the *distance* the bullet penetrates depends on the energy. Here then in this controversy the energy principle emerges for the first time.

It was not until 1807 that Thomas Young proposed the name

energy and in 1856 Lord Kelvin named it *kinetic energy*. Still later Coriolis made it *one-half mv²*.

Although the feud between Newton and Leibniz on the invention of the calculus was bitter with insinuations and charges of "theft", each held the other in high regard. Newton referred to Leibniz as "that most excellent geometer" and "that most distinguished man". And Leibniz, when asked by the Empress of Prussia his appraisal of Newton, replied: "Taking mathematics from the beginning of the world to the time when Newton lived, what he had done was much the better half."

And so for half a century this great original thinker laboured ceaselessly and made himself immortal. It was as Leonardo put it: ". . . let your work be such that after death you become an image of immortality." Of himself Leibniz said: "I have so many ideas that may perhaps be of some use in time if others more penetrating than I go deeply into them and join the beauty of their minds to the labour of mine."

In his waning years Leibniz was all but forgotten and only one mourner followed his body to the grave.

XXIII

LEONHARD EULER

Swiss; 1703-1783

There is not in all the history of mathematics a record of performance to equal that of Euler. He was born in Basel, the home of the famous Bernoulli family, but spent most of his life in Germany and in Russia. His private correspondence he did in French but he used Latin in his strictly scholarly writing. In this he wrote the Latin form of his name, *Leonnardus Eulerus*.

At 16 he had his Master's degree at the University of Basel where Jean Bernoulli was his teacher. He was competent in music, chemistry, medicine, botany, astronomy and astrology. And he commanded oriental languages. At 20 he went to St. Petersburg as professor of physics on the invitation of Catherine I and at 23 succeeded Daniel Bernoulli, his first teacher's son, as professor of mathematics. One of the tasks before him was the construction of some astronomical tables. This, it was said, would require several months of collaboration with his Russian colleagues. Euler did it alone in three days! The severeness of the climate and the labour he gave it cost him his right eye. He was then 28. And how did he greet this affliction? "J'aurai moins de distractions." Thirty-one years later he lost his other eye.

On the invitation of Frederick the Great he went to the Prussian Academy in Berlin. This was in 1741. Here he lived in the Royal Palace for 25 years and his production of original mathematics has had no equal. He contributed nearly 100 memoirs to the Academy, left twice as many more among his papers. His total production over his lifetime was some 700 papers in addition to 45 separate volumes. His complete works would fill 16,000 pages!

His chief work was in higher algebra, the calculus and theory of functions. It is worth noting that the formula $e^{ix} = \cos x + i \sin x$ bears his name. If, now, $x = \pi$, we have $e^{\pi i} = -1$, or $e^{\pi i} + 1 = 0$. This equation possesses extraordinary meaning and beauty for it contains *all* the numbers necessary to mathematics, e, π, i, 1 and 0! It was Euler who in fact introduced the symbols e and i.

There was at this time a class of problems which, in the words of Johann Bernoulli, "challenged the most ingenious mathematicians in the whole world". These problems are called isoperimetrical. The oldest such that we know is this: find a curve of given perimeter which bounds the greatest area. This, as every schoolboy knows, is a circle. Even Pappus in the third century knew this! Now Johann Bernoulli posed one: Given two points in a vertical plane but not in a vertical line, find the path between them of shortest time. The curve answering this property is the *brachistochrone*—the curve of quickest descent. It was Euler who established the necessary mathematical principles for the solution of all such problems—the Calculus of Variations.

With every genius, tales of prodigious and amazing strength come forward. Some are apochryphal but in the case of Euler all are true. On one occasion, it was said, two of his students had completed a complicated converging series to the 15th or 17th term but they found their results different in the 50th place. Euler looked at the work, went over the calculation in his mind, and showed the mistake! It was events of this sort that led Arago to say: "He calculated without effort, just as men breathe and as eagles sustain themselves in the air."

On another occasion Euler addressed himself to the classic theorem of Fermat called the law of primes. In this Fermat says that $2^{2^n} + 1$ is prime. Fermat thought it was true but admitted that he had never proved it. Euler at once showed that the law was not true by writing

$$2^{2^5} + 1 = 4,294,967,297 = 6,700,417 \times 641!!$$

So now at age 59 Euler is totally blind. With the aid of an assistant who was a tailor by trade, Euler dictated his massive *Complete Algebra,* problems in optics, dynamics, the motion of fluids and astronomy. For 21 years he was in this total darkness. In all the history of mathematics there is no record equal to this. His extraordinary mind was quieted only with death.

XXIV

BENJAMIN FRANKLIN

American; 1706-1790

The history of electro-static phenomena has uncommon enchantment, for who can fail to be brought to mirth and amusement by Ben Franklin's utterance: "I have lately made an Experiment that I desire never to repeat." Franklin had heard of the adventures of Peter von Musschenbroek with his Leyden jar. The Dutchman had exclaimed: ". . . I was struck in the arms, shoulders and breast, so that I lost my breath and was two days recovering from the effects of the blow and the terror." He added that he would not take another such shock for the Kingdom of France! Franklin was so taken by these adventures that he sold his worldly goods—his newspaper, his *Almanack,* and his printing house—to have time to do his electric experiments.

Franklin was born in Boston. His father was a soap and candle maker and he, Benjamin, was headed for the printing trade as an apprentice to his older brother. This indenture he soon abandoned and by his frugal ways and industry prospered on his own. He played an enormous role in the Revolution and in diplomatic matters afterwards.

It appears that Ben was pretty well informed on the subject of electro-statics. He knew the work of Thales, the contributions

of William Gilbert and von Guericke with his rotating globe of sulphur. He knew about St. Elmo's fire. Stephen Gray had observed electric conduction in sticks and strings and François Dufay had found two kinds of electricity—vitreous and resinous—which Franklin named "positive" and "negative". Now he learned of the Dutch device for storing a vast amount of this sacred fluid. And he learned first-hand of the terror which lurks—lying hidden as in ambush—to burst forth with violence.

Franklin's speculations were the first to connect Leyden jar experiments with lightning and at the age of 40 Ben was totally engaged in these matters. He reported to the Royal Society: "Points have a property by which they draw on as well as throw off the electrical fluid . . . If these things are so, may not the knowledge of this power of points be of use to mankind in preserving houses, churches, ships . . . from the stroke of lightning . . . and thereby secure us from the most sudden and terrible mischief."

The Royal Society promptly set about to explore these virtues of sharp points. But King George III, troubled as he was with the affairs of the Revolution, wished no dealings with a Yankee. Accordingly he urged the President of the Royal Society to consider the virtues of spheres as ends for lightning rods. The President of the Royal Society promptly replied: "I fear, your Royal Highness, that Nature cannot be brought around by royal edict." Whereupon the King suggested that the President of the Royal Society, holding to such an opinion, ought to resign!

The episode of Franklin and his kite needs no recitation. It stands as one of the classic tales of all time. And it also ranks as a great discovery in science.

Franklin's experiments on heat conduction are the first on this subject. For this he proposes the following:

> "Take a piece of wood the size and shape of a dollar between the thumb and fingers of one hand, and a dollar in like manner with the other hand; place the edges of both at the same time in the flame of a candle; and though the edge of the wooden piece takes flame, and the metal piece does not, yet you will be obliged to drop the latter before the former, it conducting the heat more suddenly to your fingers."

So it is then, he went on to say, that glass and china cups filled with hot liquors, such as tea, can be handled with immunity, ". . . but not silver ones".

It was Franklin who invented bifocal lenses:

> ". . . I therefore had formerly two pairs of spectacles, which I shifted occasionally, as in travelling I sometimes read, and often wanting to regard the prospects. Finding this change troublesome, and not always sufficiently ready, I had the glasses cut, and half of each kind associated in the same circle . . ."

Franklin was a vegetarian. He could not eat the flesh of beasts so ruthlessly slaughtered "when they so little deserved that fate". But he was fond of fish. Now it came to pass that he was on a fishing trip and the frying of the fish "smelled so admirably" that he was torn between principle and impulse. Seeing, however, that when the big fish were opened up there were smaller ones inside he decided that if they could eat their own he could with immunity eat them!

So it was that Ben Franklin, *alias* Richard Saunders, *alias* "Poor Richard", stands as the first great name in American science. Jean le Rond d'Alembert put it all very beautifully in his epigram: "Eripuit coelo fulmen sceptrumque tyrannis"—"He snatched the thunderbolt from heaven, the sceptre from tyrants."

XXV

CARL LINNAEUS

Swedish; 1707-1778

At the turn of the 18th century a vast body of knowledge had been gathered in nearly every quarter of human thought. Physics, mathematics, astronomy—these especially had foundations solid as rock —for had not Newton been? But the great world of plant and animal life, that is, natural history, had only been touched, and what had been gathered was in chaos.

Over the centuries, from Aristotle and Theophrastus and Gessner, vast accumulations of specimens had been made but there was no order, no system, no naming. · There was a great mass of single, isolated facts, but they had no connection and no meaning. What this state of affairs needed was a man possessed of a *passion for order,* and this it found in the remarkable Swede, Linnaeus.

As a boy in Uppsala his lot was poverty. The clothes he wore were cast off by others; his shoes he mended himself. It was not seldom that he went hungry. But he had an unbounded zeal for knowledge. Although he was destined to follow his father in the clergy, he was diverted from this by reading the botany of Joseph de Tournefort. This gave him a fascination for Nature which thoroughly possessed him. He abandoned the ministry, became apprenticed to a shoemaker and finally studied medicine and botany at Lund and at Uppsala.

In the spring of 1732, Linnaeus was seized with the urge to see for himself the things of Nature in the far north country and he set out on horse for Lapland. It is easy to see him—home-made coat, hand-made boots, northward through the village of Gävle, out of Uppsala. It must certainly have been the most dramatic hour of his life. When he returned, 6 months later—he had travelled 5000 miles and brought back with him 537 specimens— he went to Holland and took his degree in medicine. Forthwith, befriended by two Dutch botanists, he reached world fame with the publication of his *Systema Naturae* in 1735. In one stroke he gave botany the proper method for description and classification.

> "How great a burden has been laid on the shoulders of botanists by disagreement in names . . . as I turn over the laborious works of the authorities I observe them busied all day long with discovering plants, describing them, drawing them . . . I find, however, among them few philosophers, and hardly any who have attempted to develop nomenclature . . ."

Seeing then the need for some fixed laws on the naming of plants, he offered his proposal. "I submit my rules. If they seem worthy to you, let them be used . . . if not, please propound something better." Mindful that his new ideas would stir disfavour, especially among those he was most anxious to please, he made it clear that what he had done was ". . . not out of malice but guided by my love of botany".

He now returned to Uppsala as professor and his teaching brought students from the most distant countries. His own enthusiasm was contagious and when they had learned his method of observation he dispatched them to remote parts to gather and name and classify the plants. In the summers, Linnaeus moved out to Hammarby, some six miles from Uppsala, where he built a house and garden, and here his students came to his lectures. The place still stands and the spirit of Linnaeus is felt on every path.

In 1753 he reached his highest flight in *Species Plantarum*. In two volumes of twelve hundred pages he described and classified eight thousand species of plants in binary nomenclature. The buttercup was now *Ranunculus acris* for all the world. Five years later he did the same for zoology in the tenth edition of *Systema Natura*. Thus it was that every living thing could be described in two Latin words which at the same time gave its relation to all others. This work became the standard for all the world and now the names of plants and animals bear the letter *"L"* reminding us that this gentle man of great simplicity lives on.

Throughout his life Linnaeus was filled with a child-like piety and regarded Nature with wonder and awe. All that lived and grew filled him with wonder and love and veneration.

Linnaeus was the first scientist to be knighted in Sweden. This was in 1753. In 1761 he was granted nobility and thereafter was called Carl von Linné.

XXVI

JEAN LE ROND D'ALEMBERT

French; 1717-1783

On the steps of the Cathedral St. Jean-le-Rond in Paris, an infant was found by one named Alembert and this is how he was named. His real parents were of high station— his father, Phillipe Destouches, was a French dramatist.

D'Alembert's genius in mathematics was apparent in his earliest years and it blossomed forth in his *Traité de la Dynamique* when he was only 26. In this masterpiece he formulated the very general dynamical principle which bears his name. On simplest grounds it may be stated thus: Let a mass m have impressed on it a force F; then on the Newtonian view $F = ma$. On the view of d'Alembert we would write $F - ma = 0$. That is to say, if a particle of mass m has at a certain instant an acceleration a, then the vector ma is called the "effective force" acting on the particle, and that vector reversed, i.e., $-ma$, the "reversed effective force". These "counter effective forces" d'Alembert called "forces of inertia". So, by d'Alembert's principle, this system of forces constitutes a system in equilibrium. Accordingly, a dynamical problem is reduced to a problem in equilibrium. The spirit and content of d'Alembert's Principle cannot obviously be put in a sentence!

For many decades before d'Alembert, it will be recalled, the great controversy on *quantity of motion* raged. The Cartesians and the Leibnizians were the great warring camps and every nation in Europe entered its champion. Do we measure a force by mv or by mv^2? The whole controversy was settled in a stroke by the genius of d'Alembert when he rightly explained that the contestants were talking about two different things!

The genius and influence of d'Alembert were felt also in another quarter in this 18th century. Jointly with Diderot he began the great French *Encyclopédie* in 1746 and this massive achievement had enormous influence in the era which could now be called the Age of Enlightenment. The contributors were all themselves geniuses of a sort—Voltaire, Montesquieu, Mirabeau, Rousseau, Euler.

On the humanistic side, d'Alembert had a view which possesses singular strength and beauty: "The art of instructing and enlightening men is the noblest portion and gift within human reach."

XXVII

JOSEPH LOUIS LAGRANGE

French; 1736-1813

Who stands as the greatest mathematician of his time? It was Lagrange. At 16 he was Professor of Mathematics at Turin (Torino) and at 19 he had solved the problem of the brachistochrone which had puzzled the mathematicians for half a century. Before he was 20 he had had some correspondence with d'Alembert and with Euler. He had indeed sent his solution of that isoperimetrical problem to Euler. Euler had already found the solution but he gave the credit to Lagrange—such was his appraisal of this young genius.

At 23 Lagrange was a foreign member of the Berlin Academy. At 25 he was considered the greatest living mathematician. At 28 he won the Grand Prize of the French Academy for solving the three-body problem of the libration of the moon. The Academy then proposed the six-body problem of Jupiter and her satellites and the sun—for which Lagrange also won the prize. At 30 he succeeded Euler as Director of the Berlin Academy and he held this for 20 years. Napoleon made him a count—Comte de Lagrange—and said of him: "Lagrange is the lofty pyramid of the mathematical sciences."

In his memoirs Lagrange made original contributions to every branch of mathematics and mechanics and set them all forth in his masterpiece *Mécanique Analytique* in 1788. Here he treated exhaustively the theory of equations, differential equations, theory of numbers. He solved the problem of integral solutions of indeterminate equations of the second degree in two variables. He laid down the theory of partial differential equations and the integration of linear partial differential equations in any number of variables. The fundamental equations which dominate mechanics bear his name.

The *Mécanique Analytique* was described by Hamilton as a "scientific poem", it was so stirringly beautiful and elegant, and Lagrange himself was referred to as "The Shakespeare of Mathematics".

With a humility which characterizes those who are truly great, Lagrange would preface his replies to a questioner with "Je ne sais pas" ("I do not know"). "I have," he said, "a great aversion to disputes." His judgment of men he put in this classic aphorism: "I have always observed that the pretensions of all people are in exact inverse ratio to their merits; this is one of the axioms of morals."

In his later years Lagrange thought that he had mastered the parallel axiom problem. He prepared a brief memoir on it and at the Academy stood to read it. In the first line or two he was struck with a flash of insight and muttered: "Il faut que j'y songe encore" ("I must contemplate this further"). With this he put the paper in his pocket. It was not heard of again.

The death of Lavoisier gave Lagrange great grief and anguish and of it he said: "Il ne leur a fallu qu'un moment pour faire tomber cette tête, et cent années peut-être ne suffiront pas pour en reproduire une semblable."[1]

.Of Newton he spoke with warmth and veneration: "If you wish to see the human mind truly great, enter Newton's study when he is decomposing white light or unveiling the system of the world."

The great Talleyrand-Périgord said all that can be said in a phrase to Lagrange's father: "Your son . . . has done honour to all mankind by his genius."

XXVIII

CHARLES-AUGUSTIN COULOMB

French; 1736-1806

The time was now coming in the history of scientific thought when refinement in experiment was a necessary adjunct to pure reason. In this quarter Coulomb demonstrated a rare mastery in experimental skill and his researches with the torsion balance which made exact measurements in electrostatics and magneto-statics possible must be regarded as the greatest achievement of the 18th century.

Coulomb was an army engineer, of a family of high social position. Because he was outspoken on a government technical report he was condemned to arrest. This, with his constant failing health, forced him to abandon all his official posts and he withdrew

---

1. "It took but a moment to make that head roll and it may well require a hundred years to find an equal."

to the country where he lived entirely for his science. Years later Napoleon restored to him his official position.

Coulomb's earliest work was on the cantilever beam and on friction. His experiments on friction were shrewdly carried out on large scale and the "laws" of friction he arrived at are indeed the very ones we know today. His exhaustive analysis of the theory of the retaining wall stands as a masterpiece of elegance and rigour. Indeed, no less a figure than Thomas Young praised it.

Coulomb's greatest single achievement was in the theory of torsion. A prize was offered by the Academy for a ship's compass. Coulomb bent his labours to this and was thus led to an interest in electricity and magnetism. His researches on the torsion of silk and hair are unparalleled for refinement and the sensitivity of his torsion balance was extraordinary. It was thus with his study of twisting fibres that he enunciated the laws of force in electro-statics and magneto-statics. The significance of this can be measured only by understanding that all subsequent advances in the subject depended on this foundation. It was on the strength of Coulomb's work that Gauss and Weber were able to build a quantitative mastery of electric and magnetic phenomena.

By means of torsional oscillations Coulomb also investigated the internal friction of liquids.

Another investigation of the greatest importance, made possible only by Coulomb's experimental genius, was the work of Henry Cavendish on the "weight of the earth". This required the greatest possible skill in quantitative observation, for the force of gravitation between two terrestrial masses small enough to handle is tiny indeed. That this measurement of such extraordinarily small forces could be made at all rested on Coulomb's laws of torsion.

Coulomb also explored the distribution of electric charge on conductors of different shapes. For this he used a "proof plane" whereby he could lift off, as it were, some of the charge. Here again the forces to be measured are of the feeblest sort.

It is then altogether fitting that France should honour her son who showed such sovereign mastery of experiment.

XXIX

LUIGI GALVANI

Italian; 1737-1798

POSTE ITALIANE 30 CENT.

I° CONGR·INTERNAZ
DI ELETTRO
RADIO·BIOLOGIA

In the Piazza Galvani in Bologna stands a statue of Luigi Galvani. In his hands he holds a frog laid out in dissection. The monument commemorates a great man and a singular event in the history of scientific thought. Coulomb had just put *electro-static* phenomena on a firm basis. Now, with some chance observations by Galvani, knowledge of another kind of electricity was born.

The discovery was made, as we say, by accident. A dissected frog lay on the table. Nearby was an electrical machine. When the nerves of the frog were touched with a scalpel the muscles contracted. Galvani was astonished by this and ". . . was inflamed with an incredible zeal and eagerness . . . to bring to light what was concealed . . ." An endless array of experiments was pursued. Once on the occasion of a flash of lightning "the muscles were thrown into violent convulsions". On another occasion Galvani observed the convulsions of a frog hung on an iron trellis.

For all these strange events there were only two possible accounts: there is electricity *in* the animal or the contact with the metals brings it about. Galvani favoured the first and declared the existence of animal electricity.

Over eleven years with hundreds of experiments Galvani put together his *De Viribus Electricitatis in Motu Musculari Commentarius.* "All of this I have thought out . . . in order that it may be considered by the great and learned . . ."

And so it was that the theory of animal electricity opened a controversy which raged for a decade. Galvani's stoutest adversary was his countryman Alessandro Volta at Pavia who proved by incontestable evidence that ". . . the bodies of animals have no concern whatever . . ." But Galvani clung to his view and ten years after his treatise was published died with bitterness and disappointment. But for all of a hundred years after, the electricity "coming out of a battery" was called " galvanic current".

Now strangely enough, although Galvani was wrong, we must not forget that the connection between life and electricity is not yet clear in this enlightened day.

Galvani was born in Bologna, began a career in theology, but turned to medicine. He married the daughter of his professor, lectured in medicine at the University, and became Professor of Anatomy and Obstetrics. In his later years Napoleon entered northern Italy but Galvani refused to take the oath of allegiance and was removed from all his professorial offices. Beloved as he was by the people and the students, efforts were made to restore him to his academic position but he died before this was accomplished.

So it was that Aloisio Galvani died with grief of two kinds—his "animal electricity" was condemned and he was forbidden to teach.

XXX

CARL WILHELM SCHEELE

Swedish; 1742-1786

Any word on the story of chemistry must begin with the ancient and mediaeval speculative philosophy called alchemy. The alchemists had but two singular ambitions: the transmutation of the baser metals to gold and the elixir of life—a universal cure of disease and the extension of life without end. It is, of course, easy to scoff at such matters but every body of knowledge has had such primitive beginnings. In the case of alchemy we have indeed accomplished one of their ambitions and we have made substantial advance in the other. When the work of the ancients is properly explored, that of the moderns must be less highly appraised.

So we had Paracelsus the Swiss physician in the 13th century who taught medicine by scanning the heavens and Andreas Libavius who wrote his *Alchemia* in Germany in the 16th. This is the first real text in chemistry. Johann Baptista van Helmont is the foremost chemist of the 17th century. When he had burned a certain weight of oak wood from which he obtained only a small bit of ash, he named the *spiritum sylvestrum* by the new name of *gas*. ("It cannot be enclosed in vessels or reduced to a visible condition.") He is probably the first to do the classic experiment where a burning candle standing in shallow water is covered with an inverted vessel whereupon the water rises and the flame goes out. In the 17th century Robert Boyle turned to chemistry "not as a physician or an alchemist but as a philosopher". His assistant Robert Hooke thought that the air used up in combustion was like that used in breathing!

Thus it was that the great issue was combustion and the theory prevailed that all combustible substances contain an inflammable "element" which is given off during combustion. This *principle of fire* was called "phlogiston".

Now there came on the scene two great chemists, one in England and one on the Continent. Joseph Priestley (1733-1804), a schoolmaster and theologian, laid the foundations of the chemistry of gases with elaborate experiments of "new airs"—"nitrous air" (nitric oxide), "alkaline air" (ammonia), "vitriolic acid air" (sulphur dioxide), *and* "dephlogisticated air". This last he discovered in 1774. It was later named *oxygen* by Lavoisier. "This gas," said Priestley, "contains no phlogiston whatever."

Carl Wilhelm Scheele was a pharmacist whose one ambition was to unfold the mysteries of combustion. In his *Chemical Treatise on Air and Fire* which appeared in 1777, he reported a vast array of experiments. One of these produced a gas. Scheele put a lighted candle in it. "No sooner was this done than the candle began to burn with a big flame and emitted such a bright light that it dazed the eyes." This gas he called "fire-air". His own record shows that this event came two years *before* Priestley's independent discovery. However the credit goes for priority, the discovery of oxygen was historic. Bunsen said of it: "The day oxygen was discovered was the real birthday of chemistry."

Of his own work Scheele said: "To explain new phenomena, that is my care, and how glad is an investigator when he finds what he has sought so industriously; it is a pleasure that fills his heart with joy."

Scheele was the seventh of eleven children and was already in his fourteenth year an apprentice and researcher. Possessed of ceaseless energy and a passionate desire for truth, he was through all his years beset with poverty. In 1775, even though he had no diploma, the Swedish Academy of Science gave him the unique distinction of membership. His life was most certainly shortened by the unhealthy working surroundings and his handling of all sorts of poisonous things. His records show that he even tasted the hydrocyanic acid which he discovered!

On the day of his death, May 26 1786, he was married to a Mrs. Pohl, an apothecary's widow, thus making possible the strange hereditary privilege which governed the selling of drugs in those days. His own phrase characterizes his work and life: "For it is only truth which we wish to know, and what joy it is to have discovered it."

XXXI

ANTOINE LAURENT LAVOISIER

French; 1743-1794

In the winter of 1774 Lavoisier heard of Priestley's "dephlogisticated air". He at once saw the importance of Priestley's discovery and in a paper before the Académie des Sciences showed that combustion is the combination of the substance with a certain part of the air. This

Lavoisier described as "the purest part of the air" or the "vital air", and later he named it *oxygen*. In 1783 he dealt the old theory a more formal blow in his *Réflexions on Phlogiston:* "Chemists have made of phlogiston a vague principle. This principle is sometimes heavy and sometimes it is not. Sometimes it passes through the pores of vessels, sometimes it does not. It is a veritable Proteus which changes its form at every instant." It was not until 1789 that the death of phlogiston was spelled out in Lavoisier's classical textbook *Traité Élémentaire de Chimie*.

But it was a hard-won victory for this monument to his genius was at once the instrument of his death. The French Revolution was ablaze, the Reign of Terror afoot. The cry of the hour was: "La République n'a pas besoin de savants" (The Republic has no need of intellectuals). So as Lavoisier caused a revolution in chemistry, so was he a victim of a political revolution. On May 8 1794, with various charges against him such as "adding to tobacco, water and other ingredients detrimental to the health of the citizens", he was guillotined. The agent of the Tribunal reported as follows: "I have been to the prison for the execution of the judgment against Lavoisier which condemned him to death. I handed him over to the gendarmarie who took him to the Place de la Revolution where upon a scaffold the aforesaid Lavoisier, in my presence, suffered the pain of death." Lagrange appraised the event in a single phrase: "It took but a moment to make that head roll and it may well require a hundred years to find an equal."

At the early age of 25 Lavoisier was elected to the Académie des Sciences and for the next quarter-century accomplished some 200 commissions, issuing reports on balloons, prisons, cosmetics, ink, upholstering, mesmerism and countless other matters. Earlier still, at the age of 22, he was awarded a special gold medal by the King for winning a competition on the problem of lighting a city at night.

At 28 he married a lady half his age and although she was only 14, she served as his laboratory assistant, as his secretary and as his hostess to men of learning from all of Europe. Since Lavoisier was a man of great wealth by inheritance, he entertained in elaborate style. Marie, his wife, learned English in order to translate the foreign scientific papers which came to him. It was in this way that he learned of Priestley's work.

On the death of Lavoisier, Benjamin Thompson, who later became Count Rumford, married his widow. The marriage was ill-fated and unhappy. The domestic travail became so severe that he soon resorted to locking out her guests and she in turn poured boiling water on his flowers! Within a year Rumford, speaking of this union and of Lavoisier, said: "He had by far the better fate."

With "The Oxygen Principle", as Lavoisier named it, the way for the 19th century was laid down. Chemistry now had a firm and formal foundation. "La chimie est une science française. Elle fut constituée par Lavoisier d'immortelle mémoire."

So this 18th century ended with the execution of Lavoisier as the 16th did with the burning of Giordano Bruno. A new day, however, was unveiling, and the darkness of these tragic events was soon overshadowed by the coming century which favoured science and learning in general.

XXXII

ALESSANDRO VOLTA

Italian; 1745-1827

Alessandro Giuseppe Antonio Anastasio Volta was born in Como and here in this little village stand two monuments commemorating this Italian gentleman and scholar. In the Piazza Alessandro Volta there is a huge statue of Volta showing him, full figure, standing beside his voltaic pile. It is a stirring thing to contemplate. And hard by Lake Como is Il Tempio Voltiano—a round marble building with a hemispherical dome, all marble inside and out—and within is arrayed nearly all of Volta's apparatus. It does indeed feel quite like a temple inside and one is stirred to awe and reverence. It is really a holy place with exalted things. At Pavia at the old University is another great array on Volta—". . . il grande fisico Alessandro Volta gloria italiana . . ."—because here Volta was Professor before he was 30. He was later Professor also at Padua.

Volta travelled a great deal; in Switzerland he met Voltaire, in Paris he met Laplace and Lavoisier, in England he met Priestley. He had a rare gift for experiment and a profound understanding of all that was then known of electrical phenomena. When he was 30 he sent to Priestley an account of his electrophorus—elettroforo perpetuo—and before the century ended electrophori seven feet in diameter were being made!

When in 1791 Galvani's animal electricity became known to him, Volta repeated Galvani's experiments and was first led to agree. Soon however he took issue with Galvani. From experiments with coins on his tongue connected by wires and with spoons of different metals, the conviction grew that it was the metals which generated the electricity. Three years later Volta took his stand against his countryman Galvani. There was no animal electricity. The effect came from the metals when wetted.

When Volta abandoned altogether the role of muscles and nerves and simply put pairs of metals in contact with wet paper or cloth, he obtained impressive quantities of electricity which he measured with his newly-designed electrometer. It was this very instrument which won him Fellowship in the Royal Society. What was most enchanting to Volta was the surprise shown by the scholars at his new discovery.

Out of these investigations came Volta's first electrochemical series and finally the voltaic cell. The voltaic pile was a logical sequence. On March 20 1800, Volta communicated the first account of this invention to the Royal Society:

"... the apparatus of which I am telling you, and which will doubtless astonish you, is nothing but a collection of good conductors, arranged in a certain manner ... 30, 40, 60 pieces, or more, of copper, or better of silver, each laid upon a piece of tin or what is much better, zinc ... such an alternate succession, and always in the same order ... that is all that constitutes my new instrument."

Interest was fired up throughout Europe. At once Napoleon invited Volta to Paris and awarded him a medal. Later Volta asked to be relieved of his professorship at Pavia. To this Napoleon replied: "I cannot agree to Volta's resignation. If he is too busy as professor let him give one lecture a year."

XXXIII

PIERRE SIMON, MARQUIS DE LAPLACE

French; 1749-1827

It is strange to discover, when looking into the lives of genius, that more often than not they were born in poverty. So it was for Laplace, the son of a poor farmer in Beaumont-en-Auge in Normandy. As a boy his genius was already recognized and at 18 his friends sent him to Paris bearing letters to the scholars and professors there. He had, in an earlier year, written a letter to the great d'Alembert (who was now himself 50 years of age) and through d'Alembert he was at once appointed Professor of Mathematics at the famous École Militaire. He was soon also made a member of the Académie des Sciences, one of only 40 members, the highest honour France could bestow. With great speed he rose to distinction and stood as one of the great men of France. In later years he presided over the Academy.

In 1796 he wrote his popular *Exposition du Système du Monde*. In this he was trying to account for the very remarkable fact that the planets all revolve around the sun in the same direction; that their orbital planes are nearly identical; that their satellites (nearly all) revolve in the same sense; that the sun, the planets, the satellites rotate on their own axes in the same sense as their revolution. His nebular hypothesis, that the solar system evolved from a rotating mass of incandescent gas, prevailed for a hundred years. (Nearly 50 years earlier Immanuel Kant put forth an identical hypothesis but did not have the mathematics to make it rigorous.)

Inflamed with the singular ambition ". . . to offer a complete solution of the great mechanical problem presented by the solar system . . .", Laplace wrote his masterpiece *Mécanique Céleste*. It was a monumental exposition in five volumes accounting for the machinery of the heavens. In preparing it for the press Laplace was assisted by the mathematician Jean Baptiste Biot and of it Biot says: "Laplace himself was often unable to recover the details in the reasoning but if he was satisfied that his conclusions were correct he inserted 'Il est àisé a voir'." And W. W. R. Ball had this to say: "Laplace . . . explains nothing . . . if satisfied that his results are correct he is content to leave them with no proof . . . he removes every trace of the analysis by which he reached his results." Which led Bowditch to cry out: "I have never come across one of Laplace's 'Thus it plainly appears' without feeling sure that I have hours of hard work before me to fill up the chasm and find out how it plainly appears."

Laplace presented a copy of his *Mécanique Céleste* to Napoleon. Napoleon, learning that Laplace had not made one single reference to God, said: "Monsieur Laplace, you have written this book on the system of the world and have never mentioned its Creator." To which Laplace replied: "Je n'avais pas besoin de cette hypothèse-la." Some time later Napoleon related this to Lagrange who exclaimed: "Ah! c'est une belle hypothèse; ça explique beaucoup de chose."

"All the effects of Nature," said Laplace, "are only mathematical results of a small number of immutable laws." Precisely the same view was declared by Einstein: ". . . Nature is the realization of the simplest conceivable mathematical ideas."

On Newton's *Principia,* Laplace had this to say: "The supreme exhibition of the individual intellectual effort in the history of the human race."

With the fullness of intellect characteristic of genius, his last words were: "What we know is not much; what we do not know is immense."

XXXIV

ANDRÉ-MARIE AMPÈRE

French; 1775-1836

It was a few years before the stormy days of the French Revolution and the Reign of Terror that Ampère was born in the little village of Poleymieux near Lyons. His only schooling was at the hands of his father and by his own reading. He studied Euler and Bernoulli and Lagrange and the great French *Encyclo-pédie* done by Diderot and d'Alembert. He thus came to know

first-hand the work of Voltaire and Montesquieu and Rousseau.
For opposing the Revolutionists his father was put to death and
young Ampère stood by at the execution. In a farewell note to
his mother the elder Ampère wrote: "Quant à mon fils, il n'y a rien
que je n'attende de lui."

Ampère's first occupation, until the age of 30, was teaching in
Lyons and in Paris. In these years he was married to a girl of
extraordinary beauty. They were passionately devoted but she died
in the fifth year of their life together. These years, Ampère related,
were the finest of his life.

At 30 he was Répétiteur d'Analyse—which is to say "tutor"—in
Calculus at the École Polytechnique and rose at once to Professor.
He was also elected to the French Academy.

Now in the summer of 1820, Oersted announced his discovery
of the magnetic effect of a current-bearing conductor. Ampère had
word of it on September 11. Within a week—on September 18—
he stood before the French Academy and gave a complete description of the phenomenon. He also predicted the interaction of
neighbouring conductors and current-bearing coils. His paper was
so well received and his own intellectual curiosity so fired up that
he devoted himself with all his energy to uncovering the laws of
electrodynamics. Indeed, in the weekly meetings of the Academy
it was this new discovery of Oersted that claimed their attention to
the exclusion of all else for the next four months and Ampère was
the principal contributor. One of the Academy members said this
of it: "I do not know whether the vast field of physics ever exhibited
so beautiful a discovery, conceived and consummated with so much
rapidity."

In 1826 Ampère gave his classic lecture at the Academy titled
*Théorie Mathematique des Phénomènes Electrodynamique unique-
ment deduite de l'expérience*. This established for the first time a
proper conception of electric current and the clear distinction
between electrostatics, electric currents and electrodynamics. And
these, the very terms we use today, were introduced by Ampère
together with galvanometer and solenoid. He gave us also the rule
of thumb which bears his name. He showed that two coils behave
as two magnetized rods and thus set down a new conception of

magnetism. With these new ideas Arago showed that non-magnetic wires could pick up iron filings.

So it was that the primitive beginnings at the hands of Galvani followed by the labour of Volta and the keen observation of Oersted were woven into whole cloth by the genius of Ampère. There was now remaining only one other conception and this Faraday uncovered in 1831.

Although he received the highest recognition throughout his living years, Ampère's life was an unhappy one and this he asserted most poignantly in the epitaph he himself chose: "Tandem Felix" (Happy at Last).

XXXV

AMADEO AVOGADRO

Italian; 1776-1856

The story of atomic philosophy rightly starts with Democritus, and Lucretius memorialized the point of view in his charming poem *De Rerum Natura* . . . ". . . things are held together linked and interwoven as though by rings and hooks". Plato and Aristotle were against the idea of atoms, and "atomic theory" was silent until the 17th century. Newton had only the briefest speculations on the subject. Philosophers, he said, should discuss it. Then came John Dalton, a stubborn Quaker, with his *New System of Chemical Philosophy* in 1808. This, along with the work of Lavoisier, constitutes the foundations of chemistry. But Dalton's atomic theory, although it pretty well established the real existence of atoms, was not well received. Berzelius endorsed it but Sir Humphrey Davy scorned it. Strangely enough, although Berzelius thought well of Dalton's theory, Dalton in turn had a violent dislike for the new symbolism which Berzelius proposed!

In the same year, 1808, Gay-Lussac proposed his law whereby gases combine in simple proportions by volume. But Gay-Lussac went unheard. What he said, however, was inspiration for an Italian who was Professor of Physics at Vercelli near Milan. In 1811 Avogadro, drawing on Gay-Lussac's observations and convinced of the atomic theory, put forth his celebrated hypothesis that equal volumes of all gases at the same temperature and pressure contain equal numbers of molecules. The strength of this assertion lay in the distinction between an atom and a molecule.

Now what Avogadro said was a marvellous and amazing revelation and it would have lifted the veil of confusion but not a single soul paid it any heed! The idea lay hidden and obscure for forty-seven years! Then, in 1858, his countryman Stanislao Cannizzaro showed the beauty and strength of Avogadro's hypothesis and the confusion about atomic weights and formulae vanished. The great Julius Lothar Meyer learning of it exclaimed: "It was as though scales fell from my eyes, doubt vanished and was replaced by a feeling of peaceful certainty." But Avogadro had not lived to hear its praise. He had died two years earlier, obscure and unknown.

So it was that this great Italian gentleman and scholar, Lorenzo Romano Amadeo Carlo Avogadro di Quaregna e di Cerreto, known to schoolboys as simply Avogadro, put down an hypothesis on which all of modern chemistry stands. He lived, it was said, ". . . the life of a philosopher of the ancient type, occupied wholly with his studies while not forgetting his duties as a citizen and father of a family."

XXXVI

HANS CHRISTIAN OERSTED

Danish; 1777-1851

The discovery made by Oersted on July 21, 1820, has been the subject of vast and entangled speculation. The question for the scholar in the history of science is this: was the observation made by chance, that is, was it accidental, or was it the result of deliberate search? For a thousand years the phenomena of electricity and magnetism were known of, but there was never the slightest hint that they might have a connection. Of course, before electric currents, no connection could be observed although the work of Coulomb showing identical laws suggested some hidden connection. It was then Volta's battery which opened up the inquiry, for here, for the first time, was an electric current.

In 1774 the Bavarian Academy offered a prize for an essay "On the identity of these two mysterious forces . . ." The essays submitted filled 13 volumes from all of which the Academy sifted this conclusion: "Although some experimenters prove electricity and magnetism the same in some respects, they are dissimilar in others; they must therefore of necessity be considered distinct."

Oersted was probably the first to investigate seriously Volta's "pile" and it was during a lecture that the surprising event occurred. On connecting a wire to the battery with a compass needle near by ". . . he was struck with perplexity to see the needle make an oscillation". When he inverted the direction of the current the effect was again observed, transverse and in the other direction. "Thus it was that the discovery was made . . ." If indeed he had been looking for an effect he had no conception how it would be. Some historians contend that Oersted was seeking to demonstrate *no* connection between electric currents and magnetism. However it was, we might well end all conjecture with the phrase by Pasteur: "In experiment, accident favours the prepared mind."

Oersted was born on the island of Langeland off Denmark. His father was an apothecary and not over-prosperous. From his earliest years young Oersted was an assistant in his father's shop which led him to an interest in chemistry. At 22 he got his doctor's degree in medicine. In 1806 he was Professor of Physics at the University of Copenhagen. His discovery in 1820 brought him great honour and he was at once among the most eminent and influential men of his country. In his later years for his retirement, he was given a country house in a great park but he died before he moved to it.

It was nearly 20 years after Volta's note to the Royal Society that Oersted saw his magnetic needle move. His interest now stirred, he built himself a huge "Galvanic Apparatus" consisting of 20 enormous copper tanks filled with acid and water and with a zinc plate hanging in each one, "in order," he said, "to make a further study of the effect". He explored every possible arrangement, the magnetic needle now under the conductor, now over it, now near, now far. He interposed different materials and found the effect still showed through glass and wood and water and stone. He used needles of brass and glass and found these uninfluenced. Armed with the evidence of exhaustive experiments he sent out his report written in Latin—as befitted a scholar—*"Experimenta circa effectum conflictus electrici in acum magneticam."*

The astonishment this paper stirred has never been equalled. The discovery precipitated an avalanche. The event must now stand among the most memorable in all the history of science.

So it was that the movement of a magnetic needle had incredible consequence, for it was only the beginning. When Michael Faraday heard of it—that scullery boy in the Royal Institution—he wrote in his notebook: "Change magnetism into electricity." And this he did eleven years later and it changed the world!

XXXVII

CARL FRIEDRICH GAUSS

German; 1777-1855

In all the history of mathematics there are few who can stand beside the genius of Gauss. His father was a brick-mason, his home-life most plebeian. At the age of three he had already showed his precocious mind. He said of himself that he knew how to reckon before he could talk! At the age of ten an event occurred in his school which Gauss enjoyed telling in his later years: The Professor, Büttner by name, gave this problem: *Find the sum to 100 terms of 81297 + 81495 + 81693 + ... + 100899.* Gauss at once wrote down the result and uttered, "There it lies." The rest of the class toiled on for an hour. Only one slate was correct. It was that of Gauss. Büttner then made his classic declaration: "He is beyond me. I can teach him nothing more."

At the age of 12 Gauss was already wondering about the foundations of Euclidean geometry and at 16 he felt that there must be another kind. At 19 he solved the construction of a polygon of 17 sides by straight edge and compass alone, the first such discovery since the Greeks. At 22 he gave a rigorous proof that an equation of the nth degree has n roots and no more. At 30 he set forth his newly-discovered method of least squares. A certain astronomical problem which several eminent mathematicians said would require several months was done by Euler in three days. The illustrious Gauss solved it in one hour!

As Professor of Mathematics at Göttingen (1807) he occupied himself with every branch of mathematics. He established the mathematical theory of electricity, and his work with Weber on magnetism is classic. On one occasion the question arose as to who was the greatest mathematician in Europe. When no one answered this someone spoke up and said, "How about Gauss?" To which Laplace at once exclaimed "Gauss is the greatest mathematician in all the world." In all of his massive, profound and original mathematics not a single error has been detected. Gauss said of himself that he was "all mathematician". Leopold Kronecker appraised him thus: "Almost everything which the mathematicians of our century have brought forth in the way of original scientific ideas attaches to the name of Gauss."

To a friend Gauss wrote: "I have recently received from Hungary a little paper on Non-Euclidean geometry in which I rediscover all my own ideas and results worked out with great elegance. The writer is a very young Austrian officer, the son of one of my early friends with whom I discussed the subject in 1798. I consider the young Bolyai a genius of the first rank."

To the elder Bolyai, Gauss once wrote: "Astronomy and Pure Mathematics are the magnetic poles toward which the compass of my mind ever turns." And Wolfgang Bolyai in turn had this to say of his old friend: "The mathematical giant Gauss . . . from his lofty heights embraces in one view the stars and the abysses." This long-lasting friendship between Gauss and Bolyai, starting in their student days in Göttingen, is one of the noblest human events science can record. Indeed, when Gauss was 19 his mother asked Bolyai whether her son Carl would ever amount to anything. To which Bolyai exclaimed: "He will be the greatest mathematician in Europe."

To the Prussian Friedrich Wilhelm Bessel, Gauss once wrote this enchanting note: "I am giving this winter two courses of lectures to three students, one of which is only moderately prepared, the other less than moderately, and the third lacks both preparation and ability."

It is clear how this Prince of Mathematics viewed Isaac Newton for as W. W. R. Ball puts it: "For other great mathematicians or philosophers Gauss used the epithets 'magnus', or 'clarus' or 'clarissimus'; for Newton alone he kept the prefix 'Summus'."

So it was, he said, that "an overwhelming horde of new ideas stormed his mind" and his motto "Thou, Nature, art my goddess; to thy laws my services are bound" was his life.

XXXVIII

RENÉ LAËNNEC

French; 1781-1826

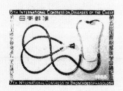

From time historic, wine merchants and inn-keepers have in a jiffy told the contents of a keg by tapping it with their knuckles. In the middle of the 18th century an Austrian physician, Leopold Auenbrugger, applied this simple method to the body, and this tapping with the fingers, known as percussion, is used this very day. Auenbrugger's discovery met with little favour and he was beset with envy and malice and hate.

Thus by the pitch or other character of the sound emitted does the physician learn of things in the parts beneath. Another method of "hearing" what goes on in the cavities of the body is auscultation, long known and practised. In this the physician puts his ear directly to the chest or abdomen and this practice is called "immediate auscultation". These methods were, up to 1816, the only ones available to the physician.

Now in 1816 a young French physician, René Théophile Hyacinthe Laënnec, reported an event in his practice which possesses a unique charm and character. He was consulted by a young female showing symptoms of disease of the heart. Because of her stoutness he could tell nothing by percussion. Her age and sex prevented him from putting his ear to her chest. He at once called to his mind an acoustic phenomenon which was well known, namely, if you scratch one end of a wooden beam with a pin, say, the sound can be heard distinctly at the other end by placing the ear there. In a flash he took up a sheaf of paper, rolled it into a tight roll, put one end against her chest and with his ear at the other end listened to her heart. "I was both surprised and gratified at being able to hear the beating of the heart with much greater clearness and distinctness than I had ever done before by direct application of my ear."

And so it was that this quiet gentleness and delicacy of a young French doctor who thought it rather improper to place his ear on the bosom of a young female, brought him to this wonderful invention. The method of hearing with the aid of a stethoscope (from the Greek *stēthos* meaning "chest") is properly designated as "mediate auscultation" and this indeed was the title of Laënnec's book, *De l'auscultation mediate*.

Laënnec proceeded to improve the instrument—his first nothing more than a roll of paper. "An entirely solid body is the best instrument for listening to the heart . . . Paper, wood and cane appear preferable . . . The dimensions are not altogether un-'important . . ."

As a physician Laënnec had great competence and skill. He was an expert in tuberculosis and in pathologic conditions of the heart and lungs. For this his new instrument was especially significant. Persons of high station were his patients, among them Chateaubriand and Madame de Staël. His own life was cut short by the very disease he knew so much about—tuberculosis—most certainly contracted from his patients. And it was one of his own students who watched the progress of the disease with Laënnec's own stethoscope.

XXXIX

NICOLAS LÉONARD SADI CARNOT

French; 1796-1832

REPUBLIQUE FRANÇAISE

18 +6

SADI CARNOT
1837-1894

Among all the aspects of physical thought, there is none which makes more demand on the intellectual process than the subject of thermodynamics. It is one of the classic hurdles for students of physical theory at every level. Not only does it call for the sharpest command of physical phenomena but also for a lofty competence in the highest forms of mathematics. It calls indeed for a kind of thinking not found too often among ordinary mortals!

Now the steam engine, as a working machine, has a long history. Hero of Alexandria in the 2nd century B.C. had one. The first "useful" engine came some 2000 years later, that of Thomas Savery in 1698. In 1769 James Watt patented his on principles which still stand in modern engines. But why it worked was not really understood nor was it ever asked how good can it be. These questions distinguish the practical man from the theoretician—the doer from the thinker. It is difficult to say how these two different aspects of human activity are to be appraised.

So it was that the *scientific understanding* of this mechanism claimed the interest of a young Frenchman known simply as Carnot. As the birthright of men of science goes, Carnot's heritage was exceptional. His father, Lazare Nicolas Marguerite Carnot, was a great French general and statesman, known as Le Grand Carnot. He was Napoleon's minister and chief of the defence of France. His brother was a renowned French writer; another Carnot, Marie François, became President of France.

Sadi Carnot studied at the École Polytechnique, spent a few years in the military and devoted the rest of his brief life to the study of the *theory* of the steam engine. He died of cholera at 36. So great was his contribution to physical thought that Ernst Mach declared: "The course of science would have been greatly altered if Carnot had not died of cholera in 1832." And Peter Guthrie Tait, of Scottish fame, put it this way: "Without this work of Carnot, the modern theory of energy, and especially the branch of it which is at present by far the most important, the dynamical theory of heat, could not have attained its now enormous development."

The question to which Carnot addressed himself was this: What happens in a steam engine at work? Carnot was aware that no one understood the theory. In his one and only paper titled *Réflexions sur la puissance motrice du feu et sur les machines propres à dévelloper cette puissance* (Reflections on the Motive Power of Heat) Carnot in 1824 showed this to be the principle: the heart of the matter is a difference in temperature and a flow of heat; "Everywhere where there is a difference of temperature, and where a flow of caloric can be effected, the production of motive power is possible."

Thus he laid bare the fundamental idea of the heat engine. He even anticipated the reversibility of the cycle: ". . . wherever this power arises it is possible to produce a difference of temperature . . ." This principle now drives our refrigerators.

So with penetrating insight into the workings of Nature—by pure reason alone—Carnot laid down the foundations of thermodynamics. Inherent in all of his work was the great generalization of energy conservation with which are interwoven the names of Clausius and Kelvin and Gibbs and Boltzmann and Mayer and Joule and Helmholtz.

XL

NIELS HENRIK ABEL

Norwegian; 1802-1829

It was Alexander Pope who said: "Who dies in youth and vigour, dies the best." And Disraeli declared: "Almost everything that is great has been done by youth." So it was that this young Norwegian, felled by tuberculosis at the age of 27, killed in the flower of his age, stands as one of those whose lives ought rather to be measured by their actions than by their years.

Despite the poverty of his youth from which in all his brief years he never once escaped, he gave his mind to mathematics to the exclusion of nearly all else. Mathematics was his constant occupation and his singular delight. When others are reading "fairy tales" Abel had already read Newton and Euler and Lagrange and Gauss.

At the end of the 16th century the general algebraic equation of the first four degrees had been solved. The solutions were algebraic and no irrationals other than radicals appeared in the solutions. Those of the first and second degree had been solved in antiquity; those of degrees three and four in the 16th century. The solution of the cubic and the quartic is associated with the names of Tartaglia, Cardano, Ferrari, Bombelli and Scipione del Ferro, an array of disputatious, unscrupulous, eloquent adversaries and scoundrels known equally well for their perversity as for their mathematics.

There remained now the solution of the fifth and higher degrees but the labour of two centuries was of no avail. Lagrange dared to express his doubt that an algebraic solution could be found but a doubt is not a proof! The evidence and history awaited the genius of Abel who proved in 1825 that general algebraic equations of the fifth and higher degrees cannot be solved algebraically. This was the celebrated theorem of Abel, his first great mathematical adventure. He had indeed done it at 19, so it is said, and Gauss, hearing of it, refused even to think about it, claiming it "another monstrosity". Abel had little regard for Gauss thereafter. It should be said that Abel's theorem established the impossibility of obtaining an algebraic solution for the general equation of degree five, and higher. It did not say that non-algebraic solutions were unobtainable. These were indeed subsequently obtained by Hermite and Poincaré.

Another of Abel's classic achievements was his proof of the very general binomial theorem, where, say, in $(x + 1)^n$, both n and x are complex.

One of the classic problems of the 18th century was to calculate the lengths of curves. Bernoulli had posed such a one, the solution of which was the brachistochrone. These involve functions and integrals of a special kind, known as elliptic. Whereas trigonometric functions are simply-periodic, elliptic functions are doubly-periodic. Abel's memoirs on elliptic functions established him as the founder of this chapter in mathematics history. The terms "Abelian integral" and "Abelian function" fix the honour.

The behaviour of a series is a fascinating thing in mathematics. What, for example, is the sum of the *endless* collection of terms $1 + \frac{1}{2} + \frac{1}{4} + \frac{1}{8} + \ldots$? This sum cannot be obtained by just adding, for no matter how many terms are added there still remain others to be added. But the sum of this series is 2! The series is said to converge. The infinite series of $1 + 2 + 3 + 4 + \ldots$ diverges. Strangely enough, the infinite series $1 - \frac{1}{2} + \frac{1}{3} - \frac{1}{4} + \ldots$ also converges. The strangeness of such series really first appeared in the Paradox of Zeno and the tale of Achilles and the Tortoise. In the days before Abel the manipulation of these series led to the weirdest results which prompted Abel to declare: "The divergent series are the invention of the devil, and it is a shame to base on them any demonstration whatsoever. By using them, one may draw any conclusion he pleases and that is why these series have produced so many failures and so many paradoxes . . . I have become prodigiously attentive to all this . . ." It was Abel's attentiveness to these enchanting inquiries that led to Cantor and Dedekind and the uncovering of strange new things.

It was, then, Newton who stood alone in the 17th century; in the 18th stood Euler, Lagrange, Laplace and d'Alembert. The 19th shone with a glittering array—Gauss, Cauchy, Jacobi, Riemann, Hamilton, Weierstrass, Hermite, Poincaré, Galois, Sophus Lie, Bessel, Fourier. These were the great masters. And among them the youngest was Niels Henrik Abel, his brilliance and genius as great as his years were few. He left enough, it is said, to occupy mathematicians for 500 years! And when asked how he had done so much he replied: "By studying the masters, not their pupils."

XLI

JOHANN BOLYAI

Hungarian; 1802-1860

In the last years of the 18th century, there were at Göttingen two students who were very close friends. They were Carl Friedrich Gauss and Wolfgang Bolyai. Long after their university days together they continued their friendship and their mutual interest in a classical problem of geometry: Euclid's Fifth Postulate. In an incessant exchange of letters they made attempts at a proof, each in his own way. Bolyai, at last convinced of his solution, sent it to Gauss in a tract titled *Theoria Parallelarum*. Gauss replied at once that it was wrong and pointed out the error. Once again Bolyai sent a new proof to Gauss but Gauss did not reply. Thus discouraged, Bolyai put aside the problem.

Now on December 15 1802, Johann Bolyai was born. His father, Wolfgang, wrote at once to his old friend Gauss: "He is, Heaven be praised, a healthy and very beautiful child, with a good disposition, black hair and eyebrows, and burning deep blue eyes . . ."

The young Bolyai, schooled by his father, was led naturally to an interest in the theory of parallels, and the Fifth Postulate consumed him with zeal and curiosity. His father urged him to leave the problem alone, recalling, we suppose, his own contest with that stubborn enigma. But before he was 18 Johann had already formulated his new geometry in which Euclidean was a special case.

When he was 21 young Bolyai wrote to his father relating his plan to publish a work on parallels. His path, he said, was not yet quite clear but "I have discovered such wonderful things that I was amazed . . ." And he added: ". . . out of nothing I have created a strange new universe." A few years later the manuscript was published. Gauss received it and forthwith wrote to his friend the elder Bolyai: ". . . and the results he has come to coincide almost exactly with my own meditations which have occupied my mind for nearly 35 years . . ." It was Gauss' intention not to publish his own work in his lifetime but to commit it to paper so that it would not perish with him. Now he wrote to his friend: "So I am greatly surprised to be spared this effort and am over-joyed that it happens to be the son of an old friend who so outstrips me in such a remarkable way."

Strangely enough, this letter from Gauss did not please the younger Bolyai, for now he learned that another had made the same discovery. He even suspected that some of his own ideas had somehow reached Gauss earlier. To add to his suspicions, he learned also that Lobachewsky, the son of a Russian peasant, had discovered non-Euclidean geometry. But after a time he abandoned these suspicions and wrote: "The nature of real Truth, of course, cannot but be one and the same in Maros-Vasarhely as in Kamschatka and on the Moon, or, to be brief, anywhere in the world; and what one finite, sensible being discovers can also not impossibly be discovered by another."

Thus it is that even genius suffers the weakness of human-kind. And Bolyai's *Science of Absolute Space* stands as the most extraordinary two dozen pages in the history of thought.

XLII

WILLIAM ROWAN HAMILTON

Irish; 1805-1865

One cannot recite the achievements of Hamilton, especially those of his boyhood days, without feeling a deep sense of awe and wonder. The question that we must ask is: how could he do it?

His schooling was all at home until he entered Trinity College in Dublin at age 19. And what had he done in the years before? At 3 he read English with superior competence; at 4 he was a good geographer; at 5 he read and translated Latin, Greek and Hebrew and was able to recite Milton and Homer; at 7 he mastered French and German; at 10 he commanded Arabic, Sanskrit, Chaldee, Syriac and Chinese. At 13 he boasted that he had mastered one language for each year of his life! At 14 the Persian Ambassador came to Dublin and young Hamilton gave the welcoming address in Persian. In this same year he mastered the Calculus and read the *Principia* and Laplace's *Mécanique Céleste*. In this masterpiece he discovered an error and his essay on it shocked the scholars!

When at 19 he came to Trinity his fame had preceded him and some declared that another Newton had come. At 22 he was made Professor of Astronomy—still an undergraduate—and became the Royal Irish Astronomer.

Before he was 18 he had begun his work in optics and at 23 published his classic Theory of Systems of Rays in which he disclosed "some curious discoveries". His great invention was his Quaternions, an algebra of rotations in space of three dimensions. The quaternion obeys the associative and distributive laws but not the commutative law. Thus, $A \times B = - B \times A$. Strangely enough, Hamilton had the belief, bordering on the occult, that his quaternions were the key to the mathematics of the physical universe.

259

Not far from the Royal Observatory in Dublin runs a canal. Over the canal is a bridge. On the lower foundation of this bridge is a plaque unveiled not long ago by Eamon de Valera, and the plaque reads: "Here as he walked by on the 16th of October 1843, Sir William Rowan Hamilton in a flash of genius discovered the fundamental formula for quaternion multiplication $i^2 = j^2 = k^2 = ijk = -1$ and cut it on a stone of this bridge."

As a man he was warm and friendly and especially fond of animals. On occasions he took overmuch to drink and made the singular mistake of getting drunk at a scientific dinner! But with all his "sins" he was knighted and the ceremony, we are told, went like this: Hamilton steps forward—the King addresses him—"Kneel down, *Professor* Hamilton"—Hamilton kneels. The King performs with the gesture of the sword and speaks again: "Rise up, *Sir* William." At 32 he was President of the Royal Irish Society.

Besides some 60 huge books in manuscript he left a mass of essays and papers in utter confusion.. For his epitaph he chose to be judged "a labour-loving and truth-loving man".

Of all the men of history Hamilton appears to have admired Fourier (Jean Baptiste Joseph Fourier) for he wrote an ode entitled *"To the Memory of Fourier"*.

> "Fourier, with solemn and profound delight,
> Joy born of awe . . .
> . . . .
> I gaze upon thy glory and grow bright:
> As if irradiate with beholden light;
> As if the immortal that remains of thee
> Attuned me to thy spirit's harmony,
> Breathing serene resolve and tranquil might.
> . . . .
> Darkness and error fleeing far away,
> And the pure mind enthroned in perfect day."

XLIII

CHARLES ROBERT DARWIN

English; 1809-1882

In 1798 the Reverend Thomas Robert Malthus wrote his *Essay on Population*. His thesis was this: the human race must one time outrun its means of subsistence and it is only by famine and pestilence and war that it can be kept within bounds. By these means the redundant are eliminated.

In his autobiography Darwin acknowledges his obligation to Malthus for while Malthus emphasizes the struggle for food, Darwin extends the meaning to the struggle for existence, a struggle

261

in which by natural selection there must be a survival of the fittest. "In October 1838," Darwin writes, "I happened to read for amusement Malthus on population, and being well prepared to appreciate the struggle for existence which everywhere goes on . . . it at once struck me that . . . favourable variations would tend to be preserved, and unfavourable ones to be destroyed. The result of this would be the formation of a new species. Here then, I had a theory by which to work."

When this flash of insight came to Darwin he was uniquely equipped to make full use of it. His father was a doctor of high station and his grandfathers (one of whom was Erasmus Darwin) men of competence. Charles Darwin himself was educated in medicine at Edinburgh and at Christ's College, Cambridge, for Holy Orders. He signed on, in 1831, on the voyage of H.M.S. *Beagle* for an expedition to South America and Australia. This journey lasted five years during which Darwin saw the inter-dependence of all living things and compiled a mass of notes bearing on the transmutation of species. Some months later he read Malthus and in it found his clue to a theory. With this idea holding him tenaciously he spent twenty years collecting facts and making experiments. He bred pigeons, studied the transport of seeds, gathered evidence of the distribution of animals. His love for truth and his great calm and honesty gave him supreme ability. "I have steadily endeavoured to keep my mind free so as to give up any hypothesis, however much beloved (and I cannot resist forming one on every subject), as soon as facts are shown to be opposed to it."

At this very same time a countryman, Alfred Russell Wallace, was exploring the fauna and flora in the Malay region. Wallace had just read Malthus and he too got the very same idea that had so gripped Darwin. He wrote a letter to Darwin saying exactly what Darwin had already thought out himself. Because of the warm regard they had for each other, Darwin was unwilling to seize the right of priority which his twenty years' study had given him. And Wallace in turn praised Darwin's "untiring patience in accumulating and that wonderful skill in using large masses of facts of the most varied kind". Darwin, he said, was ". . . of all men now living, best fitted for the great work he has undertaken and accomplished."

So by arrangement with the Linnaean Society both were properly honoured. On November 24 1859, Darwin's *The Origin of Species* was published. Its principal theme was "survival of the fittest".

Criticism and controversy world-wide was aroused. Such a theory of evolution was devastating to long-standing philosophic and religious landmarks. But some protagonists with courage carried the fight. Huxley—Thomas Henry Huxley—called it "a flash of lightning in the darkness" and when he had mastered the central idea exclaimed: "How extremely stupid not to have thought of that."

In 1863 Huxley came forward with his *Man's Place in Nature*. Darwin, in his *Origin of Species,* had not considered mankind, so Huxley, with exhaustive anatomical evidence, showed that man in body and brain differed from some apes less than apes differed among themselves! With this man was placed as the first Family in the Order of Primates.

Now in 1871 Darwin published his *The Descent of Man*—The Evidence of the Descent of Man from Some Lower Form. "We must acknowledge that man with all his noble qualities . . . with his godlike intellect . . . still bears in his bodily frame the indelible stamp of his lowly origin." Thus it is that we proceed from fishes to amphibians to reptiles to birds to mammals to MAN. So was wrought an intellectual and religious upheaval that has had no likeness in the history of human thought.

As a boy at school, so we are told, Darwin was "rather below the common standard of intellect" but his interest in Nature was insatiable. The story goes that one day while catching beetles he had one in each hand and seeing a third which he wished to capture he thrust one into his mouth. The imprisoned one ejected some foul fluid whereupon young Darwin spat him out and thus lost two! From such events is genius awakened.

XLIV

URBAIN JEAN JOSEPH LEVERRIER

French; 1811-1877

In all the history of physical thought there is nothing more impressive, more sublime, more satisfying to the intellect, more possessed of grandeur, than mathematical prediction. By this we mean the prediction of pure mathematics that certain physical phenomena exist. The rareness of these attests to their character and their greatness.

In 1781 Sir William Herschel, while examining some stars in Gemini, observed what he thought was a comet. With further study and computation of its orbit he found it to be a planet. It was named Uranus, god of the skies. Its discovery doubled the boundaries of the known solar system, since Saturn was the last and most remote planet known to the ancients. Galileo had raised a problem about it: "Ultimum planetam tergeminum observavi."

Now, as is the custom in astronomy, the path of Uranus was at once followed painstakingly and some 40 years later slight departures were noticed. The actual orbit was not in agreement with theory. During the next twenty years this discrepancy grew alarming, still, however, a triflingly small angular separation of some 100 seconds of arc! To astronomers this in intolerable. A great stir arose and a deep disquiet. Can our laws of motion be wrong? Is our mathematics sound? Maybe Newton's Law of Gravitation needs revision! Maybe Newtonian mechanics is not to be relied upon. So it was no small matter to be put aside. It was serious to contemplate.

The idea was now advanced that this strangeness in the motion of Uranus might be due to the attraction of a still more remote planet—one yet altogether unknown. The problem then is clear:

find this unknown planet. Such a problem raises unbelievable mathematical difficulties, so difficult and laborious indeed that Sir George Airy, Astronomer Royal of England, offered the opinion that the problem is very likely invincible. This it might have been but for the courage of two young mathematicians, one in England, the other in France. The Englishman, John Couch Adams, while still an undergraduate at Cambridge, undertook the calculation and finished it two years later. He sent on his results to the Royal Observatory where, since they had never heard of Adams, his communication was put aside.

Across the water in France the Secretary of the Paris Observatory, Dominique François Jean Arago, suggested to a young colleague that he attack the problem. This young Frenchman, Urbain Jean Joseph Leverrier, was Professor of Astronomy at the École Polytechnique and had continued the work of Laplace in celestial mechanics. So, on Arago's invitation and without knowledge of things across the sea, he made his own calculations, resting them, as did Adams, on the assumption that Newton's gravitation held good for the interaction of Uranus and another planetary body more remote. He sent them forthwith to the Observatory at Berlin. There, on the very night they arrived, the young German astronomer Johann Gottfried Galle, then only 34, turned his telescope to the sky. Within the hour and less than one degree from the precise position Leverrier had calculated he found the planet.

So it was that on September 23, 1846, Newtonian mechanics had its greatest triumph. The mathematical discovery of Neptune based on mathematical prediction—which is pure reason alone—stands as a classic monument to the perfection of Newton.

Some 20 years later Maxwell predicted by an array of equations pure and precise that certain waves must exist. Heinrich Hertz gripped by their beauty and their physical meaning found the waves. In 1905 Albert Einstein predicted on mathematical grounds alone that light is deviated in a gravitational field. Photographic evidence obtained in the eclipse of 1919 revealed the truth of the prediction.

These three singular events bear witness to the deep and abiding strength and beauty of mathematical prediction. Such achievements reveal the highest pinnacles of man's intellectual life. None can transcend them.

XLV

HERMANN VON HELMHOLTZ

German; 1821-1894

On July 23 1847, a 26-year-old German Army surgeon, son of a poor schoolmaster, stood before the Berlin Physical Society and read a paper. It was a sensation for the scientific world. It established for Helmholtz a foremost place among the scientific thinkers of all history. It ranks as one of the most important contributions of the 19th century. The paper was titled *Ueber die Erhaltung der Kraft* (On the Conservation of Energy).

The magnificent structure of this idea was first formulated by Julius Robert Mayer in 1842. Two things directed his thinking: when the pulp in a paper factory was stirred it got hot and Nature must have some other laws than just those of Galileo and Newton! So in a paper in Liebig's *Annalen*, Mayer proposed the equivalence between certain kinds of energy and heat. His new idea met with a hostile reception. Even the German periodicals ignored him. So tortured was he by these events that he sprang from a window in a sleepless night and although hurt in the legs he recovered only to suffer a severe depression. He sought comfort in a sanatorium and reports flew about that Mayer had died in a lunatic asylum! The only champion he had was John Tyndall. Thus was a great man broken in body and spirit for thinking anew.

Across the Channel a 22-year-old, God-fearing Victorian gentleman named James Prescott Joule was giving a few lectures to the Royal Society. His first one connected heat and electricity. He had also done a paddle-wheel experiment which produced his memoir titled *On Matter, Living Force, and Heat*. It was at this Oxford Meeting that Joule and Lord Kelvin were brought together and this was the beginning of forty years of sublime and unclouded friendship. Indeed, had not William Thomson, later Lord Kelvin, been at the session, Joule's paper would have fallen into obscurity. Years later, in 1895, when Lord Kelvin unveiled a statue of Joule, he said: "I can never forget . . . when I heard a paper read by a very unassuming young man who betrayed no consciousness in his manner that he had a great idea to unfold. I was tremendously struck with the paper . . ."

Now came Helmholtz. Mayer had the *idea;* Joule did the *experiment*. What this new conception needed was a rigorous mathematical demonstration showing the extent of its validity. Helmholtz, with his rare aptitude for mathematics—and he had not studied mathematics at all in the University—examined all the domains where this conservation principle played a role—in mechanics, in heat, in electricity, magnetism, physical chemistry, astronomy. He even showed that Faraday's new scheme of electromagnetic induction agreed with the new doctrine—that cutting lines of force requires work. The rigor and eloquence of his paper at once gave Helmholtz unparalleled eminence. He became a pillar of German science.

So Mayer had been rejected and died broken in spirit. Joule was quite disregarded except by Thomas. And Helmholtz aroused two camps hostile with each other, one defending experiment, the other theory.

Helmholtz—his full name was Hermann Ludwig Ferdinand von Helmholtz—had studied medicine at the Friedrich Wilhelm Institute in Berlin. He showed a sovereign command of all domains of knowledge. His professorial career has hardly had an equal: Professor of Physiology at Konigsberg in 1848—here he invented the ophthalmoscope which allows the retina of the living eye to be seen. "Helmholtz has unfolded to us a new world," exclaimed a colleague. In 1855 he was Professor of Anatomy at Bonn; in 1858 Professor of Physiology at Heidelberg; in 1871 Professor of Physics at Berlin. He made original contributions in physiological optics, in the mechanism of sight and colour vision, in hearing, in music and in hydrodynamics.

Unlike the classical German scientific papers which are massive and burdensome to read, Helmholtz wrote with a warm and inviting phrase. In his essay *On The Sensation of Sound in General* we read: ". . . the soughing, howling, and whistling of the wind . . . the splashing of water, the rolling and rumbling of carriages . . . the seething of a waterfall . . . the rustling of the leaves in the wood . . ." These words are like poetry and men of science have seldom said it with such grace and elegance.

XLVI

GREGOR JOHANN MENDEL

Austrian; 1822-1884

In the Spring of 1900 three botanists, de Vries in Holland, Correns in Germany and Tschermak in Austria, each without knowledge of the discovery of the others, simultaneously unearthed a paper which had lain obscure, forgotten and dust-ridden for 35 years. This paper had been written by an Augustinian monk after eight years of diligence and labour on the peas which he grew in the monastery garden. He had read the paper before the Brunn Society of Natural Science in the spring of 1865 and it had been sent to the best scientific libraries in all the world: London, Berlin, Rome, Vienna, Uppsala, St. Petersburg—and to America. How it fell to such complete obscurity can never be known. It may be that the great controversy over Darwin's new theory obscured all other matters. However it was, Mendel died unacclaimed in his own lifetime, with sore and bitter disappointment that no one had the least interest in the great secrets of nature which he had unfolded.

Born of peasants in Moravia, his early schooling was brief because of ill health brought on him by over-work. The task of earning his bread and studying at the same time was too much. His one ambition to become the village schoolmaster had thus to be abandoned. At 21 he joined the Augustinian Order and was ordained a priest. His hope and talent still lay in teaching and he stood examination for a village post in physics and natural history. This he failed. Six years later he tried it again and failed again. The rest of his life he devoted with ceaseless passion to his flowers and plants and bees. Absorbed as he was with Nature he watched with unending patience, month after month, year following year, the germination, the growing and the flowering of his plants, one generation after another.

His principal experiments were carried out on the common edible pea. His purpose was to discover how cross-fertilization would effect such characteristics as tallness and dwarfness, and how hereditary factors retain their identity from generation to generation. He crossed peas 6 feet high with peas less than a foot high; he crossed those with wrinkled seeds with those with round seeds; he crossed yellow seeds with green seeds. His records and notes were massive in detail. The patience that this required is impossible to describe. Only a man with calm in his soul could endure this long-suffering task.

From all of this came the Mendelian laws of heredity and the foundations of genetics. Experiments on insects and fishes and snails and other creatures showed Mendel's principles to be universally valid.

As he himself wrote in his classic paper which lay so long in obscurity but which finally brought him the honour which was his due: "It requires indeed some courage to undertake a labour of such far-reaching extent . . ."

So it was that this quiet man-of-the-cloth unravelled with his peas why it is that parents with brown eyes have children with blue eyes and how a child born today may resemble an ancestor far remote.

XLVII

LOUIS PASTEUR

French; 1822-1895

About the middle of the 19th century an anguished cry was heard across all the nation of France: The sheep are dying here; the silkworms are dying there; the wine is turning bad. Later in the century a little boy, Joseph Meister by name, was bitten by a dog, and his death was inevitable.

Before the time of Pasteur, disease was an inscrutable mystery. Plague and pestilence came with a suddenness and felled tens of thousands. The greatest scourge of all time was the Black Death in the 14th century which wiped out entire populations. And then there was scurvy and leprosy and the Dancing Mania and the Sweating Sickness. For these things the only explanation was devils and demons and the only cure casting them out.

Another question hotly debated was spontaneous generation. How did new living things come to be? Some said that living things could come only from other living things and some said that toads just came out of the mud! Aristotle stood for spontaneous generation and Aristotle was strong. Leeuwenhoek in the 17th century was against it and Lazzaro Spallanzani in the 18th was against it. But the great Lamarck—Jean Baptiste Pierre Antoine de Monet de Lamarck, Chevalier in the 19th century—favoured it.

On this scene came Louis Pasteur, son of a tanner. At the

Sorbonne he was inspired by the great French chemist Jean Baptiste André Dumas and for all his life chemistry was his passion.

With great insight and unending patience Pasteur attacked the new problems. For five years, beginning in 1859, he made his memorable experiments on fermentation and proved that the yeast is the cause and that "unwanted" organic beings caused decay and putrefaction and mould. Thus, to keep the wine from going to vinegar, heat it. And so we have *pasteurization*.

Now the request came to look at the devastating silkworm disease in the south of France. "Oh," said Pasteur, "I have never handled a silkworm," to which his great teacher Dumas replied: "All the better." And after another five years of labour, done with patriotic devotion, he found the cause and the cure. In quick succession he attacked anthrax which killed the sheep and the cholera which killed the fowl. The germ theory of disease was now on solid ground.

Inspired by Pasteur's work, Joseph Lister laid down the principles of antiseptic surgery. Robert Koch and his pupils discovered one after another the bacillus of typhoid fever (1879); the bacillus of tuberculosis (1882); the cause of diphtheria and cholera in 1886; the undulant fever in 1897; the bubonic plague (Pasteurella pestis) in 1898. Later the micro-organisms of malaria, of sleeping sickness, of botulism, of dysentery were discovered. Of all the years of human history these two last decades of the 19th century must stand unparalleled in triumphs for the flesh and blood.

In addition to these frightful terrors already conquered was the great tragedy which followed the bite of a mad dog. This was a human suffering that had no equal. Occasion arose for Pasteur to erase this scourge for on the 6th of July 1885, a strange drama unfolded.

There came to Pasteur three persons, Joseph Meister, aged nine, his mother, and Monsieur Théodore Vone, a grocer. Monsieur Vone and the boy had been bitten two days before by Vone's own dog. The dog had gone mad; Monsieur Vone had killed it. The boy had bites on his arms and hands and legs and thighs, fourteen severe wounds. He could hardly walk. Monsieur Vone was fortunate; although bitten his skin had not been torn. Pasteur sent him home.

Now it happened that the Académie des Sciences was in session and Pasteur invited some colleagues to see for themselves the tragedy of the little boy. They were agreed that Joseph Meister could not escape the rabies. Pasteur told of his work on rendering dogs immune by inoculation. "The death of this child appearing to be inevitable, I decided, not without lively and sore anxiety, as may well be believed, to try upon Joseph Meister the method which I had found constantly successful with dogs . . ." So, at eight o'clock in the evening, sixty hours after the bites, Pasteur inoculated Joseph Meister. He made further inoculations, thirteen altogether, over ten days.

During these terrible days Mme. Pasteur wrote to her children: "My dear children—your father has had another bad night; he is dreading the last inoculations on the child." And on another occasion: "Your father is absorbed in his thoughts, talks little, sleeps little, rises at dawn . . ."

The result of this adventure done by Pasteur with holy boldness was soon heard around the world. In this extraordinary sequence of events which saved the wine in Orleans, the silkworms in Ales, the sheep and the fowl, and the little boy from Alsace, Pasteur became the benefactor of mankind and the noblest name in France.

Even in the hour of his death his mind and heart were on his people and his land: "I am sorry to die; I should have liked to render further services to my country."

XLVIII

DIMITRI IVANOVITSCH MENDELEEFF

Russian; 1834-1907

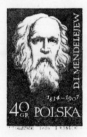 

As it was with Isaac Newton, Dimitri Mendeleeff pretty nearly did not survive his birth. Afflicted in the lungs he was given only a few months to live. He was born in Toboisk in remote Siberia, his father a Russian gentleman, his mother a Mongol beauty. When he was 13 his father was stricken with blindness and died of tuberculosis. His mother, wanting a proper schooling for her son, set out for Moskva with the hope of putting him in the University. In this she failed, so she went on to Saint Petersburg and here Dimitri did his course in science. At 32, after teaching here and there over Russia, he returned to the University as Professor of Chemistry.

It was already known that certain chemical elements bore some relation to others and some attempts were being made at classification. This systematic ordering is one of the singular hopes of science. As early as 1815 William Prout proposed that the atomic weights of all elements are exact multiples of that of the lightest, hydrogen. In 1829 Johann Wolfgang Döbereiner put the elements in groups of three—called Döbereiner's Triads. In 1866 J. A. R. Newlands proposed his law "according to which the elements having likeness in their properties exhibit peculiar relationships, like those existing in music between a note and its octave." But there were objections. It did not allow for those elements yet undiscovered. And one argued that Newlands might just as well have arranged the elements in the alphabetical order of their initial letters! So the paper was rejected. Newlands was grievously pained and was not heard from again.

Now in 1869, Mendeleeff proposed his system to the Russian Chemical Society. It is most certain that he had not heard of Newlands' idea. He arranged the elements in the order of their increasing atomic weights, pointed out the periodicity in their properties, and predicted the existence and position and properties of those yet unknown. "Just as the pendulum returns again in its swing, just as the moon returns in its orbit, just as the advancing year ever brings the rose of spring, so do the properties of the elements periodically recur as the weights of the atoms rise."

Thus with boldness and faith he set down this marvellous scheme of prediction which was in some certain instances fulfilled with a mystic accuracy. Germanium is the classic example. Some 20 years later he spoke to the Chemical Society of Great Britain: "When, in 1871, I described to the Russian Chemical Society the properties, clearly defined by the periodic law, which such elements ought to possess, I never hoped that I should live to mention their discovery to the Chemical Society of Great Britain as a confirmation of the exactitude and the generality of the periodic law."

The person of Mendeleeff was classic to behold and his singular attraction was his massive head of hair. He was indeed his country's Paderewski. It was his custom to cut his hair but once a year and even when he was presented to the Czar he made no change in his habit. His chief pleasure was reading Jules Verne.

The great British chemist Sir William Ramsay spoke of him as "that peculiar foreigner every hair of whose head acts in independence of every other". He was not unmindful of his own genius and introduced himself as THE Mendeleeff. Given much to irritability and bursts of anger he was nonetheless loved by his students and respected by everyone.

And so it was that when the English rejected Newlands' idea, the honour went to Russia.

XLIX

WILHELM KONRAD ROENTGEN

German; 1845-1923

As the 19th century drew to a triumphant close, a strange philosophy prevailed in certain quarters. Some classical physicists offered the view that all had been done, all had been discovered, nothing remained but a refinement in measurement. This must be considered one of the strangest circumstances in the history of scientific thought. But this view was short-lived for in 1895 an event was reported that literally changed the world.

On November 8 in that memorable year, Wilhelm Konrad Roentgen had an accident in his laboratory. A certain photographic plate, although well protected from light, was found fogged. His curiosity led him also to observe that a phosphorescent screen became luminous. These strange events were taking place near his work with electric discharges in highly exhausted glass tubes.

On December 28 Roentgen reported his findings in a paper titled *On A New Kind Of Rays*. These rays had the astonishing property of passing through solid matter. They could, moreover, pass through human flesh and reveal the bones. The proof of this was witnessed at once with the Chairman of the meeting as the subject. Roentgen proposed that "For brevity's sake I shall use the expression 'rays' and to distinguish them from others of this name, I shall call them 'X-rays'. " The Physical Society promptly named them "Roentgen Rays".

Quite apart from their usefulness to human kind and indeed to the study of all things, living and lifeless, this discovery opened up the era of the New Physics. The names in this new era are legion: J. J. Thomas, Sir William Crookes, Heinrich Hertz, R. A. Millikan, W. D. Coolidge, Max von Laue, Bragg and Bragg, Henri Becquerel, Marie and Pierre Curie, Rutherford, Max Planck, Albert Einstein, Bohr, de Broglie. And there is no end.

The sensation of this new discovery spread like wildfire. For many it was incredible, surpassing belief. A new kind of light passes through wood and flesh! Photographs of the bones in the hand can be made! Newspapers had difficulty in convincing the people of the truth of it. It must be magic! Stories were born; cartoons appeared:

> "I'm full of daze,
> Shock and amaze;
> For nowadays
> I hear they'll gaze
> Thro' cloak and gown—and even stays
> These naughty, naughty Roentgen rays."

In the state of New Jersey a bill was introduced: "An act to prohibit the insertion of X-rays or any device for producing the same into, or their use in connection with opera glasses or similar aids to vision." A London paper suggested that the best thing would be "to burn all the Roentgen rays", execute all the discoverers and cast all the apparatus into the sea! "Let the fish contemplate each other's bones."

The man responsible for all this tumult was a sober scholar working in a modest laboratory. He was born in the Rhineland in a tiny village into a family of modest means. His father was a cloth merchant. They moved to Holland where Wilhelm got his schooling and in an illness lost one eye. His later schooling was at Utrecht and at Zurich.

Strangely enough, he was not of a mind for learning in these youthful days and spent his time in the mountains and on the lakes and his love affair with an innkeeper's daughter diverted him altogether. But there was at Zurich one August Kundt, a physicist, who thought well of him. Wilhelm became his assistant and thus fired with the beauty of physics, at his master's hands he quickly rose to renown of his own. He was in turn Professor of Physics at Giessen—for this post Helmholtz recommended him—then at Wurzburg. It was here in his 50th year that he made his monumental discovery.

In 1901 he was awarded the first Nobel Prize in Physics for "the exceptional services rendered by him in the discovery of the special rays which have been called after him". He gave the money to his University.

The innkeeper's daughter whom he married in 1872 was his companion for nearly 50 years. In the days of his labours in his laboratory when his new discovery was soon to unfold she wrote: "I have had to go through several terrible days. My husband comes late to dinner and is usually in a very bad humour. He eats little, talks not at all and returns to the laboratory immediately after eating." When she died he lost his zeal for work and took again to his old fancy of climbing in the Alps.

So it was that an accidental observation bequeathed to man this great weapon against disease and gave to Roentgen eternal honour.

L

IVAN PETROVITCH PAVLOV

Russian; 1849-1936

Say the name and the mind responds as did Pavlov's dog when the bell rang! It is indeed not strange that when the name Pavlov is spoken the thought at once is *saliva*.

Pavlov was born in Ryazan in Central Russia. At 34 he was graduated in medicine at Leningrad and the next half-century of his life had not a moment of calm or quiet. Possessed as he was of a brilliant mind and an incomparable memory and blessed with boundless energy and spirit, he had no time for even the slightest idleness. His enthusiasm was endless and contagious and although his laboratory was little more than a shed it was a buzzing hive of unabated industry. Even with these primitive facilities men came from far to be near him. There was hardly a place in all the world where his work was not known. It was reported that his laboratory operated like an old-fashioned town-meeting—one day a week they all gathered to talk their problems and their progress. At these events he would shout and dance when some experiment was reported done and conclusive.

From 1897 on he was Professor at the Imperial Academy engaged still in his researches on the physiology of the heart, on the glands and on digestion. In 1904 he won the Nobel Prize for his work on the mechanism of digestion. In 1930 a laboratory was built for him in Koltuszi near Leningrad. It is now called Pavlovo.

His classical work on the conditioned reflex laid the foundations for the psychology of behaviour.

For science which was his passion he had the greatest hope: "Only science, exact science about human nature itself, and the most sincere approach to it by the aid of the omnipotent scientific method, will deliver man from his present gloom . . ."

For the student of science he had some advice: "Study, compare and accumulate facts. As perfect as is the structure of a bird's wing, the bird would never be able to fly if its wings were not supported by air. Facts are the air of the scientist; without them you would never be able to fly. Without them your theories are useless efforts . . . Learn the ABCs of science before ascending its heights. Never reach for the next step before having mastered the preceding one."

LI

ANTOINE HENRI BECQUEREL

French; 1852-1908

The name Becquerel is one of the most honoured in all France. Three in the family were physicists of renown—Antoine César (1788-1878); his son Alexandre Edmond (1820-1891); and his son Antoine Henri.

It was January 1896. Roentgen's new x-rays had just stirred the world. Jules Henri Poincaré, the great mathematician, was reporting Roentgen's discovery to the French Academy. The discharge tube producing the x-rays had shown fluorescence.

This instantly invited the interest of Becquerel for his father and his grandfather had all done meritorious work on phosphorescence. Perhaps x-rays are related to these luminescent phenomena? Within a month Becquerel had uncovered another strange event. Using a compound of uranium and potassium he reported as follows: "I wrapped a Lumière photographic plate . . . with two sheets of thick black paper, so thick that the plate did not become clouded by exposure to the sun for a whole day. I placed on the paper a plate of the phosphorescent substance and exposed the whole thing to the sun for several hours. When I developed the photographic plate I saw the silhouette of the phosphorescent substance in black on the negative . . . We may therefore conclude from these experiments that the substance in question emits radiations which penetrate paper that is opaque to light."

A week later his results were even more exciting. Since the sun was not shining he kept his arrangements all prepared in the dark in the drawer and when he developed the plates he found the images very intense. "I at once thought that the action might be able to go on in the dark." And this was correct. Thus was uncovered the so-called *Becquerel Rays,* the spontaneous emission of minerals containing radium.

Now the interest in Roentgen's x-rays was so intense that little attention was paid to Becquerel's discovery and had it not been for the curiosity of a young Polish girl this great event might have fallen into obscurity. Thus it was that this spontaneous disintegration of solid stuff, named "radioactivity" by Marie Curie, created another stir in the scientific world and exposed for the first time the *inside* of the atom.

In 1903 Becquerel shared the Nobel Prize with the Curies for "The special services rendered by him in the discovery of spontaneous radioactivity".

Events now came one upon another in such quick succession as to make them nearly impossible to chronicle. In 1909 Sir J. J. Thomson likened the effect of the new discoveries "to that produced in literature by the Renaissance". And he saw with prophetic wisdom "In the distance tower still higher peaks, which will yield to those who ascend them still wider prospects, and deepen the feeling,

whose truth is emphasized by every advance in science, that 'Great
are the Works of the Lord'."

LII

JULES HENRI POINCARÉ

French; 1854-1912

It is likely that the name of Poincaré is less
known than any we might mention except, of
course, to those few in science and mathematics
and philosophy who have themselves reached
the highest flights. It was, for example, the
like of Planck and Einstein—if there be a
like—who rested their own thinking on the
epistemology of Poincaré. *What knowledge is
certain?* is the principal question. Poincaré's
treatise titled *The Foundations of Science*
explores this query with a cold, unyielding
rigour and an unassailable logic which disarms even the boldest
intellects.

Now, strangely enough, Poincaré showed no special ability in
mathematics in his early years. More than that, certain tests
disclosed that he was of very low intelligence! Worse still, his
eyesight was utterly poor and his temper vile. In this matter he
was like Alexander the Great whose temper was his greatest enemy!

But Poincaré was blessed on every other count—he had good
ancestry, the provisions for his schooling were the noblest sort,
and he had the great gift of prodigious memory, little less indeed
than miraculous. As one views the giant intellects in mathematics
in the centuries preceding it is nearly impossible to name any who
knew *all* the mathematics of their own time. Newton very probably
knew all that preceded him and Gauss commanded all the
mathematics of the centuries before 1800. Certainly in the year

1900 it would be dangerous to make a claim but it is true nonetheless that Poincaré embraced the entire subject! This, by the way, was said of Enrico Fermi with respect to physics—and in the middle of the 20th century!

So at age 27 Poincaré was Professor at the University of Paris. The Chairs he held bespeak the loftiness of his mind—celestial mechanics, the calculus of probability, mathematical physics. Altogether he wrote some 500 original memoirs in higher algebra, function theory, theory of orbits, the three-body problem. To those bold new concepts of quantum theory and relativity he gave his singular support, a higher praise than which could not be found.

On the pursuit of science he had this to say: "The scientist does not study nature because it is useful; he studies it because he delights in it, and he delights in it because it is beautiful. If nature were not beautiful, it would not be worth knowing, and if nature were not worth knowing, life would not be worth living." The beauty to which Poincaré refers is "that profounder beauty which comes from the harmonious order of the parts and which a pure intelligence can grasp".

So here again two centuries later we meet with Newton who put it so: ". . . and whence arises all that order and beauty which we see in the world."

On the lighter side, in his essay on *Mathematical Creation,* in which he himself played no small role, he speaks with reverence of Gauss: ". . . a geometer of genius and a very precocious and accurate computer", and in the next sentence, "As for myself, I must confess, I am absolutely incapable even of adding without mistakes."

LIII

HEINRICH RUDOLPH HERTZ

German; 1857-1894

The conception of a *field* is a very important conception in physics. For example, the space —the region—around the Earth, is a *gravitational* field. Gravitational forces can be detected in it. The gravitational field of the moon is a weaker one, the gravitational field of Jupiter greater. The gravitational fields of certain stars are enormous. So too these fields may be described in terms of their energy density. So it is that a charged body or a magnetized bar demonstrates—gives rise to—a field in its vicinity. The ancient view of this "action at a distance" was that some material, cloudy "stuff", made connection between the bodies, a rather occult point of view. In the 18th century this intervening medium was abandoned when Newton's gravitational forces were thought to act through empty space.

Now in 1820 Oersted observed the magnetic effects of a current-bearing conductor and 11 years later Faraday used magnetism to produce electricity. Thus these two strange forces were found to have a connection. Faraday now filled the regions around magnets and charged bodies with *lines of force*. Now James Clerk Maxwell put Faraday's ideas into mathematical form—a set of *field equations* which predicted some very strange things. Whereas a steady current in a wire gives rise to a steady electromagnetic field, that is, E and H are constant at any point, a changing current, say an increasing one—which means that the charges in the wire are being accelerated—will send out a pulse of energy which spreads everywhere with the velocity of light. This he gave to the Royal Society in his paper *On a Dynamical Theory of the Electromagnetic Field* on December 8, 1864. Maxwell's original equations were twenty in number with twenty variables—a terrifying thing to contemplate. They now exist as four and bind together with beautiful precision and conciseness the phenomena of light and electricity and magnetism. Indeed, his dynamical theory predicted "that light itself is an electromagnetic disturbance . . ."

Now this momentous prediction solely on the basis of Maxwell's extraordinary mathematical insight lay quiet for more than twenty years. One reason for this might very well be that few could understand it! Indeed, the Irish physicist George Francis FitzGerald published a paper titled *On the Impossibility of Originating Disturbances in the Ether by Means of Electric Forces!*

Heinrich Hertz was born in Hamburg where he had his early schooling. He studied at Munich, read Laplace and Lagrange, and at 21 came under the spell of Helmholtz in Berlin. Within a year he won a prize with a paper titled *Kinetic Energy of Electricity in Motion*. In 1887 he was led to contemplate the "physical structure" of Maxwell's equations. Whereas others had troubled themselves with the purely mathematical, gymnastic Hertz tried to penetrate the physical ideas. If Maxwell says there are waves we should be able to find them!

His apparatus was primitive. The two spheres on an old induction coil gave him his spark gap; with proper potential, an oscillatory spark occurred. If what Maxwell said was right, an electromagnetic wave should go out. For a receiver he had another gap—just a circular loop of wire with a metal sphere on each end. It worked! Thus were electromagnetic waves first sent and detected. Hertz also proved that they could be reflected, refracted, polarized, diffracted—just as light—and, *mirabile dictu*—they had the same velocity!

So these Hertzian waves confirmed all of Maxwell's predictions. And thus it was that radio was born. Now Lodge in England and Popoff in Russia extended the investigations yet strangely enough not one of these, nor indeed Hertz himself, saw that this was a means of communicating without wires. Sir William Crookes, some four years later, predicted it and Guglielmo Marconi achieved it. But even Marconi was led nearly to put the idea aside for, said he: ". . . the idea was so elementary, so simple in its logic, that it was difficult for me to believe that no one else had thought of it."

As an aside to his experiments on Maxwell's waves Hertz made another significant discovery. When his spark gap and the spheres were exposed to light the spark could bridge a longer gap. This was the first hint of the photoelectric effect.

In 1889 Hertz succeeded the great Clausius—Rudolph Julius Emanuel Clausius—as Professor of Physics at Bonn. And here at the youthful age of 37 he was felled by blood-poisoning, one of those whose lives must be measured not by the years but by the actions.

When now at every turn we hear the radio and the television and the broadcast of the satellites we should contemplate a moment the wonder of it all and the spirit of Heinrich Hertz which brought it to pass.

LIV

MAX PLANCK

German; 1858-1947

One of the most profound if not indeed one of the most revolutionary ideas in all the history of physical thought bears on the problem of a "hot poker". If you heat a poker in a fire or if you watch a blacksmith heat an iron in his forge, the iron first gets "hot"—you may "feel" it is hot but it still looks the same as cold—then it gets *red,* then it becomes *white hot* and then it may get *bluish* in colour. If now the radiation from this hot iron is examined spectroscopically nearly all the beautiful colours of the spectrum are seen. It is really quite a dramatic thing to witness.

To study these phenomena the physicist has invented in his mind what is called a "black body". This is simply an ingenious little box-like furnace with a hole in it and the radiation escaping through the hole approximates the physicist's need for "black-body radiation".

Now the distribution of energy in this black-body radiation was the subject of long study by a great array of able men—Gustav Robert Kirchhoff (1824-1887), Robert Wilhelm Bunsen (1811-1899), Lummer, Pringsheim, Wien, Lord Rayleigh. These were men of sovereign competence but a great contradiction between theory and experiment plagued them all. This dilemma was resolved by the bold and brilliant assumption of Max Planck put forward by him to the Berlin Physical Society on October 19 1900.

Known as the *Quantum Postulate* it said that a body does not radiate energy continuously but rather intermittently, in discrete finite bundles called "quanta". The single quantum, moreover, has the energy hf where f is the frequency of the radiation, that is, the frequency of the atomic oscillator, and h is a universal constant. This new theory at once gave the correct answer to the radiation problems but it was a severe contradiction to the classical physics of Newton and Maxwell. For some it was a violent departure and too great a break with "orthodox" physics, but within days this revolutionary idea was on solid ground. Indeed, Rubens in Berlin that very night found that his experimental data fitted the new formula. Some days later Planck himself made final the value of his "quantum of action" h which is a pretty tiny number—

6.55×10^{-27} erg-seconds. Its "nature" is also strange, being as it is the product of energy and time. And a further strangeness: it has the same "nature" as angular momentum!

The role subsequently played by Planck's h is too vast to chronicle. The photo-electric effect, Bohr's theory of the hydrogen atom, the Compton effect, the de Broglie wavelength of matter, the Uncertainty Principle—all bear witness to the profoundness of the idea. Indeed, Planck himself, so it is told, said to his son: "I have made a discovery today as important as Newton's."

Planck's life was long and full both with great achievement and with tragedy. He was born in Kiel of a long family of scholars. He studied at Munich and at Berlin and was Professor at both. He was Secretary of the Prussian Academy of Science and President of the Kaiser Wilhelm Society. This was the highest academic post in all Germany. In 1920 he received the Nobel Prize. It was through his influence that Einstein came to Berlin and together they stood as the noblest team of theoreticians in the first years of the 20th century. A classic photograph shows Nernst, Einstein, Planck, Millikan and von Laue at Einstein's home where they often gathered to play music. So it was that Planck's life was filled with joy and the fullness of his own achievement and the company of colleagues, each himself a monument in science. But on the other side was grief and tragedy for in his long years—nearly 10 decades —he saw the horror of two World Wars both engulfing his own country. In the last one he pleaded with Hitler for protection of his non-Aryan colleagues. In the first one he lost two daughters and a son and in the second one another son was executed by the Nazis. If adversity gives a man character then Max Planck had a fullness thereof.

Said Albert Einstein: "A man to whom it has been given to bless the world with a great creative idea has no need for the praise of posterity. His very achievement has already conferred a higher boon upon him."

Very recently a 2-mark coin was minted in Germany showing the face of Planck. Thus it is that this great man whose thoughts transcended those of ordinary mortals, is made known to all the people of his land.

LV

MARIE SKLADOWSKA CURIE

Polish; 1867-1934

Her maiden name was Marie Skladowska. She was born in Poland but came to Paris at 23 to study. At the Sorbonne her chief interest was science, the while living in a garret with the most meagre means. At the Paris School of Physics and Chemistry was a poorly-paid professor, Pierre Curie. They met, they courted; in 1895 they were married. The new Becquerel Rays from uranium took her attention—this subject was her doctoral dissertation—whereupon she set out to test the "activity" of other elements. She found that some substances were even more active than uranium and thorium and conjectured on the existence of a new element. Pierre Curie realized the importance of this conjecture, abandoned his own research and joined her in four years of sheer physical travail.

From the Bohemian uranium mines came one ton of waste in burlap sacks, the first batch to be separated. Altogether it was six tons of this pitchblende ore on which they laboured incessantly in an abandoned shed with a leaky roof. And out of this all they

288

got was less than one-tenth of a gram of pure radium! The cauldron they used could handle some 40 pounds and in this Marie stirred the boiling mass in the heat of summer and in the cold of the winter. "And yet," wrote Marie Curie, "it was in this miserable old shed that the best and happiest years of our lives were spent, entirely consecrated to work."

Their first success they announced in July 1898, in very modest terms: "We have attempted to isolate this substance in pitchblende . . . We obtained a substance whose activity is about 400 times greater than that of uranium . . . We believe . . . that the substance contains a metal which has not yet been known . . . If the existence of this new metal is confirmed, we propose to call it *polonium,* after the name of the native country of one of us."

In December of that same year the Curies issued another report. A new substance had been unearthed "its activity 900 times that of uranium . . . The various reasons which we have presented lead us to believe that the new radioactive substance contains a new element, to which we propose to give the name radium."

For this monumental patience and labour they received the Nobel Prize in 1903 jointly with Henri Becquerel. Their first use of the money was for an assistant and a better shed. They now had one daughter, Irène, six years old. The next year, 1904, Eve was born. Both were to become accomplished. one, Irène, to share in a Nobel Prize with her husband Frederic Joliot in 1935.

The news of polonium and radium stirred the scientific world. Becquerel found some of the new radiations to have the property of electrons with a velocity about half that of light. A few weeks later in January 1899 a brilliant New Zealander, Ernest Rutherford (later Lord Rutherford of Nelson) reported on other rays from uranium—". . . there are at least two distinct types of radiation— one that is very easily absorbed, which will be termed for convenience ἇ radiation, and the other of a more penetrating character which will be termed the β radiation." It was so stirring a bit of news that Marie Curie exclaimed: "I would advise England to watch Professor Rutherford; his work on radioactivity has surprised me greatly."

There came immediately another report by Paul Villard of a still more penetrating radiation emitted by radium which he called (γ) gamma radiation. In the wake of all these events the theory of radioactive transformation was proposed by Rutherford and Soddy.

So now their lives together were rich with reward and the whole world honoured them. Pierre Curie was Professor of Physics at the Sorbonne. He lectured at the Royal Institution and they jointly received the Davy Medal of the Royal Society. On one occasion, on the arm of the venerable Lord Kelvin, they went to banquet in the Royal Hall. Here were gathered the men and women of highest station to do them honour. But all that the Curies could do was look in amazement at the dress and jewels and contemplate how many laboratories they could equip with this wealth!

But this noble and wonderful life together was torn asunder by a great tragedy. In the spring of 1906 Professor Curie was crossing the wet street in Paris with his mind elsewhere. He slipped—and in a flash a horse-drawn carriage had run him over. So now alone with her work and her children, dressed usually in black, Mme. Curie lived in a deep and private quiet. The great Rutherford never failed to remark how much her spirit had been stilled and how ill she looked. But withal she continued her work and in 1911 was again made Nobel Laureate for her achievements in chemistry.

In 1922 she came to America to receive an extraordinary gift— one gram of radium. In 1936, now imperiled by 30 years of exposure to radiation, she died of anaemia. Her life with Pierre and her life alone stand as the greatest single human drama in the whole history of science.

Said Albert Einstein in a memorial: "It was my good fortune to be linked with Mme. Curie through twenty years of sublime and unclouded friendship. I came to admire her human grandeur to an ever-growing degree. Her strength, her purity of will, her austerity toward herself, her objectivity, her incorruptible judgment —all these were of a kind seldom found joined in a single individual."

LVI

ALBERT EINSTEIN

Jewish; 1879-1955

How does one abbreviate the significant events in the life of this man? How in a page or two do we tell his physics and his philosophy? How do we communicate his feeling, his compassion, his judgment of other men and events? It cannot indeed be done. We elect, therefore, to give the highlights in outline.

SOME EVENTS IN THE LIFE OF ALBERT EINSTEIN

March 14, 1879: Born in Ulm, Bavaria, of German-Jewish parents. Hermann Einstein, his father, operated an electro-chemical factory with his brother. Pauline Koch, his mother, serious and artistic. Albert no child prodigy. Disliked physical exertion. Especially disliked playing at being a soldier.

291

1880-94:   Spent in Munich. Attended the *Gymnasium* until 16. "The teachers appeared to me like sergeants." Read Bernstein's *Naturwissenschaftliche Volksbücher* and Büchner's *Kraft und Stoff*.

1894:   Family moved to Milan (Italy) but Albert stayed to complete his course at the *Gymnasium*. He found it more and more intolerable to be compelled to memorize. Teacher speaks: "Your presence in the class destroys the respect of the students." Albert fled to Milan.

1896-01:   Studied at Zurich Polytechnical School. Impressed the director with his knowledge of mathematics. His aim already: To discover the simplest rules by which to comprehend natural laws. Hermann Minkowski, lecturer in mathematics.

1901:   Swiss citizen. Worked at the Patent Office in Bern. First marriage to Mileva Maritsch, a fellow-student. Two sons. Wife blunt and stern; his life neither peaceful nor happy. (Separated in Berlin in 1913.) Reads Mach, Poincaré, Kant, Hume.

1905:   Papers on Quantum Theory, Relativity Theory, Brownian Motion. First paper on Relativity titled *Electrodynamik bewegter Körper*.

1909:   Professor at Zurich University.

1910:   Professor of Theoretical Physics at the German University in Prague. Aversion to formality and ceremonial. Appointed by Emperor Franz Josef of Austria on recommendation of the Faculty. Emperor demands that Einstein belong to a recognized church. Einstein simply wrote that his religion was "Mosaic".

1912:   Professor of Theoretical Physics at Zurich. Paper: *"Über die thermodynamische Begründung des photochemischen Aquivalenzgesetzes."*

1913:   Moved to Berlin. Wilhelm II founds Kaiser Wilhelm Institute. Max Planck and Walter Nernst invite Einstein. Title of Professor unencumbered by any obligation except that of lecturing as much or as little as he desired. Physics Colloquium every week:

Einstein — Planck — Nernst — von Laue — James
Franck — Hertz — Lise Meitner — Schrodinger —
and such visitors as Poincaré — Rutherford — Langevin — Lorentz — Madame Curie.

1914:   World War in August. Neutral Belgium invaded by
German troops. German Government demands of its
intellectuals that they proclaim their allegiance with
the German military. The famous "Manifesto"—the
assertion that German culture and German militarism
are identical. Einstein would not sign it. Einstein
meets his cousin Elsa whom he knew as a child in
Munich. She a widow with two daughters; maternal
temperament. Einstein marries Elsa.

1916:   General Relativity finished. Astronomer Royal points
out that on March 29, 1919, a total eclipse in Brazil
and Africa would permit conditions for testing
Einstein's theory.

1919:   November 7, London TIMES headlines — "The
Glorious Dead" — "Armistice Observance" — "All
Trains in the Country Stop". On the same day:
"Revolution in Science" — "Newtonian Ideas Over-
thrown". Remarks by Eddington, Whitehead, J. J.
Thomson. Sir Oliver Lodge hoped that the observations would decide *against* Einstein's theory! When
the evidence was heard he said: "It was a dramatic
triumph."

1919-32:   Visited USA, England, France, China, Japan, Spain,
Palestine. Lectures — lectures — lectures.

1932:   Nobel Prize: "This prize is awarded to Professor
Einstein for the photo-electric law and his work in
the field of theoretical physics."

1933:   Resigned from the Prussian Academy. Comes to
Institute for Advanced Study. Offered posts throughout the world . . . Madrid, Jerusalem, Sorbonne . . .
Invitation to Institute for Advanced Study: "Professor
Einstein—I would not presume to offer you a post
in this new Institute, but if on reflection you decide
that it would afford you the opportunity which you

value, you would be welcome on your own terms."
Einstein comes to Princeton, USA.

1945:   Official retirement.

1949:   Unified Field Theory — Generalized Theory of
                 Gravitation.

April 18,
1955:   "He now belongs to the ages."

SOME REMARKS REVEALING THE ENCHANTMENT OF RELATIVITY

Let us say that for our ordinary purposes the earth stands still.
But remember: it is whirling through space in a frightening way.
It rotates at about 1000 miles per hour; it goes about the sun at
about 20 miles per second. The whole solar system is moving
within our own star system at some 15 miles per second and our
star system is moving in the Milky Way at some 200 miles per
second and the Milky Way is drifting to some remote galaxy at
100 miles per second. It is enough to make your head spin!

Now you have sat in a train in a railway station. You are at
rest on your seat; the train is at rest in the station. Then suddenly
you look at another train—and you are moving! Or are you not?
Or picture yourself on a ship on a calm sea or in a jet aircraft
flying calmly high above the earth. What experiment can you do
to detect your motion?

Or you are swimming in a fast stream. When you go downstream
the current aids you; when you go upstream the current opposes
you. Now stand on a fast, fast vehicle and shine a light now ahead
of you now behind you. Or stand on the edge of the earth and do
this—as Michelson and Morley did it. Will the ray of light go
faster when going ahead than when going backward?

Or you are riding on the rooftop of a fast train and your friend
stands by the track. The lightning flashes, hitting the front and
rear ends of the train. The strikes are simultaneous. Do you
and your friend see them simultaneously?

All these strange and puzzling events become clear with our
understanding of Relativity.

Now further still: clocks and measuring rods behave strangely
when moving *fast*. Clocks slow down and measuring rods shrink!

Imagine it: at 90% of the velocity of light your measuring rod would shrink to half its length; at the velocity of light it would shrink to nothing! But its mass, *mirabile dictu,* would increase! And your clock? At *c*—the velocity of light—it would stop!

So you say that all this ravages common sense and reason. We say that what you need now is a new kind of common sense and Relativity makes it all clear and persuasive.

SOME REMARKS REVEALING EINSTEIN THE HUMANITARIAN

On Paul Langevin—*In Memoriam:*

> "The news of Paul Langevin's death dealt me a greater blow than most of the events of these fateful years . . . Langevin was endowed with unusual clarity and agility in scientific thought . . . It appears to me a foregone conclusion that he would have developed the Special Theory of Relativity had that not been done elsewhere; for he had clearly perceived its essential aspects. I can only give expression to my gratitude for having personally known this man of purity and illumination."

On Walther Nernst—*In Memoriam:*

> ". . . his brief remarks gave evidence of a truly amazing scientific instinct combined both with a sovereign knowledge . . . and a rare mastery of the experimental methods."

On Mahatma Gandhi—*In Memoriam:*

> "Generations to come, it may be, will scarce believe that such a one as this ever in flesh and blood walked upon this earth."

(A note concerning the stamps shown here: Among the great human beings whom Einstein admired with deep feeling and with manly affection two stood out above all others—Rabindranath Tagore and Mahatma Gandhi. Indeed, as I recall it, there were on the wall in Einstein's study in his home only two photographs and these were of Tagore and Gandhi. The reason for the Langevin stamp is already obvious in Einstein's *Memoriam* to him.)

Epilogos

In our *Prologos* we set forth the purpose and the hope in this monograph. It must avail me little to plead the largeness of my design as an excuse for an imperfect execution of its particulars. But a feeble effort is better than no effort at all and if our purpose is achieved in any degree we are much rewarded.

It is our singular hope that your brief adventures in these pages have given you some pleasant hours and the ambition to know more about these men who changed the world. It may indeed come to pass that one of you, filled with the fire of curiosity and the will to know, possessed as by a demon with a spirit of untiring labour, will one day be honoured as we honour those whose names are on these pages.

J.S.M.

APPENDIX

SOME
ENCHANTING
QUESTIONS
FOR
ENQUIRING MINDS

by

Julius S. Miller

Some Enchanting Questions for Enquiring Minds

Once before, in the month of January 1963, I had the singular good fortune to lecture in Professor Messel's Summer Science School for High-school Students in the University of Sydney School of Physics. That event and events subsequent to it I must view as one of the great intellectual adventures of my career. The spirit of the audience was terrific and their alertness to my demonstrations and questions and to my philosophy of learning was rewarding to my soul. My lectures then, as in the present summer school, were all on demonstrations in physics—demonstrations of the simplest sort—with sticks and string and sealing wax. And I posed a multitude of questions for the young students to ponder and contemplate.

On my return to my home in California letters came by the score from those children and my reward reached new heights. Indeed, I proposed to certain quarters in Sydney that some of those letters be published. I sent copies of some to Professor Messel, for reference was made repeatedly to "the wonderful thing that Professor Messel is doing for the children of Australia". All spoke of the problems we had raised in the lectures and Marylin East put it this way: "I hope that you have invented many new problems that will make people 'struggle from the neck up' . . . I was touched by the beauty and drama of your simple experiments and problems . . . Some of the things you have shown us opened a new outlook for me . . . I still can't quite realise that these are so simple yet so interesting; there is a world full of these little things and so many people ignore them and more tragically, some have never heard of them."

So it was clear to me and my conviction of long years was supported . . . what I have said before is true: our principal business must be to stir interest, awaken enthusiasm, arouse a curiosity, kindle a feeling, fire up the imagination. And this is best accomplished by a dramatic demonstration which is filled at once with some enchanting questions.

303

Thus I am brought to the substance of this appendix which I first wrote for the Reserve Bank of Australia magazine "Currency" and which I reproduce here by courtesy of that publication for your interest. The demonstrations or observations I leave to you. Those you can do you should do. You *must*, I say, listen to the gurgle of a brook and watch a bird fluff up at evening time. And you should have some tea leaves in your cup when you stir it! But all the demonstrations need not be done. YOU CAN IMAGINE THEM—and imagination is one of the most important ingredients in the thinking of the man of science and of the poet.

And now to some questions. My intention here is clear—Those who read these pages should engage themselves and their families and friends and their colleagues and everybody, in the intellectual gymnastic. The questions and assertions and dilemmas also make delightful "dinner-talk" and "after-dinner-talk". They will, we hope, divert the mind from the ordinary conversation. They are, I say, *something to think about*. And they bear on the world about us which is so filled with wonder and beauty and drama.

We must never forget Newton's view of it—". . . whence arises all that order and beauty which we see in the world".

1. In breaking a stout string it is found that a *sudden* pull on it succeeds where a steady pull does not. What do you make of this?

2. Someone says to me: "How much does the Earth weigh?" To which I reply: "As much as *you* do." What do you think of this?

3. When sand or gravel or the like is dumped from the truck the pile assumes a conical shape. Which lies in the steeper cone—coarse gravel or fine sand?

4. Suppose that you, a physicist, shoot a polar bear on the Arctic ice. You are equipped with a rope but no scale or devices with which to weigh him. How could you approximate his weight?

5. The work done by the heart per day is of the order of 25,000 kilogram-meters! Contemplate this fantastic matter.

6. An hour-glass rests on a beam balance and is counter-balanced with a weight W. The sand is in the upper half. Discuss the behaviour of the balance when motion of the sand begins, as it flows, and when the last sand has fallen into the lower chamber.

7. Two men in a crowd are pressing against each other and each complains that it is the other who is doing the pushing! What must a physicist say?

8. Wheelbarrows may have iron wheels or rubber-tyred ones. Why is the rubber-tyred one easier to push?

9. Human beings know several kinds of mechanisms of locomotion: walking, as on legs; flying, as with wings; swimming, as fish in the sea; crawling, as worms do; jumping, as rabbits; by propulsion, as squid do it. Can you *imagine* other means of locomotion?

10. Pour yourself a cup of tea *with tea leaves in it.* Now stir with a spoon. Where are the tea leaves when you first take away the spoon? Where are they finally? What do you make of this?

11. You pour water from a jug. It goes glub-glub-glub. Molasses does better. Account for this sound and for change in pitch as the liquid empties.

12. Next time you play billiards or "pool" note well this fact: that the height of the cushion is $\frac{7}{10}$ the diameter of the ball. Why do you suppose *this* is?

13. Consider this: you drop a steel ball on a glass plate and it rebounds *so* high. What will be the result of dropping a glass ball on a steel plate?

14. Think out how a simple pendulum would behave in an elevator.

15. A sheet of paper can resist formidable tension but still can tear easily. Think about this.

16. Young's modulus for human bone is about the same as that for steel—some 30×10^6 lbs./in.^{2}! This is fantastic!

17. It is usually thought that the time to push a kid in a swing to produce large amplitude is at the end of each swing. This is not true! The pushes should be timed to reach their maximum force when the displacement from equilibrium is least. Explore this.

18. Some tobacco cans are elliptical (roughly) in cross section. If they are squeezed into cylindrical (roughly) cross section the volume grows. Explore this problem!

19. Raise your hand. The veins in the back of it disappear. Why?

20. The number of molecules in a cubic centimeter of air at 0°C and 76 cm. of mercury is about 3×10^{19}. Imagine each molecule to be a grain of sand. We would then have about ONE CUBIC MILE of sand! Suppose you counted these at the rate of 10 per second. How long would it take you to count them?

ANSWER: One hundred thousand million years! Prove it.

21. If your fireplace smoked up your living room what could you do about it?

22. In the Alps the cottages have enormous boulders—enormous rocks—atop their roofs. Can you think of a reason for this?

23. Pieces of paper nearly always fall in still air with faces horizontal, not edge-on. Why is this?

24. It is very difficult to make mercury enter a fine-bore tube. Why do you suppose this is?

25. Consider this fantastic device: A very fine bore capillary tube rests in a liquid. The liquid can climb to a height **h** in a tube of this bore. But the tube is *less* than height **h** whereupon the liquid overflows. This overflow operates a machine!

26. A blotter hangs from a support. The lower end rests in a vessel of water. After a time the water has "climbed" up the blotter. Its potential energy is therefore increased. Where did the energy come from?

27. Drop some drops of water on a very hot hot-plate. They sizzle and run about in a most chaotic fashion, diminishing in size through rapid evaporation. When *very small*, however, they nearly cease getting smaller and continue to dance about madly on the hot-plate. The tiny tiny ones have extraordinary life. It is all a wonderful thing to see. What would you say about it?

28. Put a fresh stem of celery or rhubarb in a vessel of coloured water. What happens is wonderful to behold.

29. Two identical balloons are each filled—one with H and the other with He. Hydrogen is half as dense as helium. How do their "lifting powers" compare? Note that we put "lifting powers" in quotations.

30. The composition of the atmosphere at the top of a mountain is practically the same as at the base and yet nitrogen is lighter than oxygen and might be expected to float on the denser gas. How does this happen?

31. Do *you* believe that atoms exist? How would you convince an unbeliever?

32. Explain precisely how it is that the air in an automobile tyre supports the weight of the car.

33. In a picnic box cooled with dry ice the grapes tasted peculiarly but the bananas did not. What's going on here?

34. A rubber balloon filled with hydrogen quickly collapses. What do you make of this?

35. Imagine this: a cubic inch of palladium can absorb about 1,000 cubic inches of hydrogen and in this process increases in volume only about 10%. To reduce 1,000 cubic inches of hydrogen to 1.1 cubic inches would require over 900 atmospheres! Over 13,000 lbs./in.^{2}.
Is not this fantastic?

36. Sausages put in water swell; ripe cherries burst in a rainfall; strawberries left in sugar shrivel. It is all a wonder to behold.

37. Slices of raw potato become crisp in fresh water but shrink if left in salt water. And bathing in salt water increases rather than allays thirst. What do you make of it?

38. A circular iron hoop has an iron rod across the diameter—fixed solidly. The whole system is heated uniformly. What happens?

39. A metal plate has a tiny tiny hole in it. The plate is heated uniformly—as by putting it in your oven. What happens?

40. Why are thermometer bulbs cylindrical?

41. A thermocouple requires *two* metals, so it appears when you study the subject. Could you make a thermocouple out of ONE wire?

42. In the late of the day, toward evening, one sees the birds fluffing themselves up. What are they thinking?

43. The temperature of the human body is about 37°C and room temperature is about 22°C—some 15° *less*. Why don't we feel cold?

44. Shivering is a strange business. It is certainly involuntary although *some* can make themselves shiver! Its function, so it appears, is to *restore* heat losses. How do you suppose this is accomplished?

45. Why can you hold a burning wooden match in your fingers so long?

46. It is said that you can put your wetted finger into molten lead for a brief time. What is the mechanism of immunity?

47. Would a pitcher of water be cooled more quickly by ice floating at the top or by ice held at the bottom?

48. Why does a kernel of pop-corn pop when heated?

49. In making a snow-ball out of snow you can make it a ball of ice. How is this accomplished? But if the temperature of the snow is below freezing it is difficult to make a snow-ball.

50. Does ice evaporate?

51. Can we have ice denser than water?

52. Is the ice of an iceberg in the sea salty to the taste?

53. Put some ice cubes in a glass. Pour some hot tea over them. Sharp pistol-like cracking of the ice ensues. Why is this?

54. There is a certain geranium whose odour is very pronounced when a leaf of the plant is crushed in the fingers, more so by far than comes from the whole huge untouched plant. Account for this. It is remarkable.

55. When you stand near a huge cake of ice you "feel the cold". What's going on?

56. Here's a good one: Why not make the walls of your living room excellent reflectors and thus keep yourself warm by the heat energy you yourself radiate?

57. All surfaces exposed to radiation experience a pressure. Maxwell said so. And this pressure is twice as great for a perfect reflector as for a perfect absorber.

58. *"Red sky at night,*
Sailors' delight.
Red sky in the morning,
Sailors' warning."
What do you make of this?

59. *"When the clouds appear like rocks and towers,*
The earth's refreshed by frequent showers."
What do you make of this?

60. It is a simple matter to blow *hot and cold* from the mouth. But the air available is *all hot!* Explain this!

61. What happens when a plant freezes? Why is there less chance of a frost on a windy night?

62. Set a silver coin erect in a chunk of dry ice. It soon vibrates. As time goes the pitch changes. Look into this.

63. This is a philosophic conjecture: Most of *our* knowledge comes to us through sight and hearing. These are *wave* mechanisms. Conjecture on how creatures both blind and deaf would acquire a structure of knowledge of their "world".

64. Why do sea waves "break"? If you will observe them closely you will notice that the crest does not break until the height above the quiet set level is $\lambda/2\pi$. That is, they break when their height is about ⅙ the distance between them.

65. What part does the separation of your ears on your head play in the mechanism of hearing? When you speak an observer *behind* you can hear it. This is really a strange business.

66. Why does a brook gurgle?

67. Why does a whip "crack"?

68. Why does thunder "roll"?

69. Sound can be heard farther after a rain—so they say. What do you make of this?

70. The ear is a fantastic mechanism: Drop a pin from the height of a foot, say, on to a sheet of paper. You do about one ten-thousandth of a foot-pound of work! The sound can be heard across the room. Your ear receives less than one ten-billionth foot-pound of energy! How *little* is this? Well, if you used it to heat a gram of water one degree it would require some hundred million years!

71. Lord Rayleigh said: "If an observer moves with a velocity twice that of sound a musical composition would be heard *backwards* correct in time and tune." What do you think of this?

72. The earth is negatively charged. Indeed, the charge is not to be toyed with. It turns out to be some 100,000 coulombs. It is not known how this comes to be. Have you an idea?

73. A matter to observe closely: Charge a rubber rod or comb with fur. Present it to some cork dust. A large mass of the dust fixes itself to the rod. This is already a wonderful thing! Now—after a moment—some of the dust flees from the rod! It is indeed ejected with a great force. All of this is wonder to behold.

74. In electrostatic experiments and on other occasions we constantly encounter "sparks". What is it that you **SEE** and what it is that you **HEAR?** Not so easy, is it!

75. Blow an array of soap bubbles into the air. Some are charged.

76. We put a "keeper" across the "poles" of a horseshoe magnet. What does this do?

77. Recall the classical problem of a wound-up spring dissolved in acid. Where does the energy in the spring go? Now reframe this inquiry using a magnetized bar. It took energy to magnetize it.

78. The human body is a good electrical conductor. Why is this? Under the right conditions 110 volts can be fatal! As little as $\frac{1}{10}$ ampere can be fatal! Contemplate these matters.

79. Would you expect living organisms to be affected by magnetic fields? Maybe this ought to be explored.

80. Consider the floor and the two walls of the room where these meet at a corner to be mirrors. How many images can you see?

81. How tall a mirror do you need to see all of you?

82. How do you account for the sparkle and brilliance of a diamond or of a dew drop on a blade of grass in the sun? Is not a shining drop of water on a blade of grass a glorious thing to see?

83. You are swimming under water. The sun is low in the sky. What do you see?

84. Grasp an empty glass in the hand. Look at your finger tips through the glass. Now fill the glass with ice water. The glass soon gets wet on the outside. Now grasp the glass again. The finger tips are now seen through the surface of the water very very clearly—more clearly indeed than when the glass is dry.

85. Can a mirage be photographed?

86. Stars twinkle. Why does not the moon?

87. Have you ever seen the Green Flash?

88. Look into the bottom of your empty tea cup or on the surface of your glass of milk. A source of light should be overhead but not directly. You will see a bright region called a caustic. Can you figure out how it gets there?

89. The mollusk nautilus has a pin-hole camera eye. What does he see?

90. Why is the rainbow circular?

91. Coloured rings are often seen around lights shining in a fog. Why is this?

92. If you squint your eyes when looking at some light sources you see colours. What's going on?

93. A large chunk of ice in the daylight looks blue. Why? Crush it and it looks something else.

94. Why do waterfalls foam?

95. Smoke from a burning cigarette is blue; when exhaled it is white. Why is this?

96. What is the crackling and hissing sound heard in the vicinity of high voltage devices or high "tension" lines?

97. We have spoken of the fantastic sensitivity of the ear. Consider the eye: it can detect something like 10^{-10} erg! This is one ten-billionth of an erg! For light, say, about 6,000 A —which is yellow—about 100 quanta would excite the sensation of vision.

98. You hear "around a corner". Why can't you see "around a corner"?

99. Why do water waves come in parallel to the shore?

100. A certain coil spring has a modulus K, say 10 lbs./in. What modulus will *half* the spring have? More simply: If a whole spring is *so* stiff, how stiff is half of it?

101. A bubble has two surfaces. A bubble in a liquid, however, has only one surface. What are the consequences of this?

102. A lighted candle rests on the bottom of an open glass fruit jar—standing upright. The jar is dropped. What happens?

103. A lighted candle is floated upright in a vessel of water. Let us say that one inch of the candle is above water at time zero—when we start to look at things. *As the candle burns* what happens?

104. Sometimes, when you walk on the snow, it creaks. Why is this?

105. Some days the smoke from your chimney goes *up*; on other days it falls *down*. Why is this?

106. A man stands on a platform scale and weighs himself. He now takes a quick step off the platform. What does the scale read at the beginning and at the end of this motion? Careful now—everybody gets this wrong?

107. A man goes from A to B uniformly at the rate of 20 m.p.h. He returns uniformly—at the uniform rate of—30 m.p.h. What is his average rate for the total trip?

108. A man goes from A to B uniformly at 30 m.p.h. At what rate must he return to average 60 m.p.h. for the total trip?

109. Water waves of a certain wave length travel with a certain velocity. Suppose you had waves of the same wave length in a sea of mercury?

110. What is the likelihood of the human mind ever having a "true" picture of the physical world?
NOTE TO READER—I have run out of energy—not questions!